Exploring the

Limestone Landscapes

of the

Burren

and the

Gort Lowlands

GW00584977

A guide for walkers, cyclists and motorists

by
Mike Simms

Published by burrenkarst.com

Exploring the Limestone Landscapes of the Burren and the Gort Lowlands: A guide for walkers, cyclists and motorists.

Published by Burrenkarst.com
Eden House, Belfast BT8 8JY

Printed and bound by The Universities Press (Belfast) Ltd.

Acknowledgements
Many thanks to Matthew Parkes, Andy Farrant, Graham Mullan, Bernie Picton, Hugh Prudden and Alison Muir who helped in the preparation of this guide.

For further copies of this guide contact
landscapes@burrenkarst.com

WARNING: It is inadvisable to enter any cave passages, other than those of commercial show caves, except under the supervision of experienced cavers. Furthermore, some of the surface terrain may be difficult, particularly in poor weather. Anyone embarking on these excursions or entering any caves mentioned does so entirely at their own risk. Mention in this guide does not imply a public right of way.

ISBN 0-9540892-0-0

CONTENTS

Front cover: Rinnenkarren (solution runnels) on sloping limestone pavement, Clooncoose, eastern Burren.

Back cover: Black Turlough Moss (*Cinclidotus fontinaloides*) on seasonally drowned boulders at Coole Lough, near Gort.

About this guide

The Burren is a remarkable area justly famous for its limestone scenery, the abundance and diversity of its archaeological monuments, and the richness of its flora. Many books have been written about this area, with new ones appearing each year. Though some cover specific topics, such as flowers, lichens and archaeological monuments, many others provide only a superficial treatment of any one particular aspect. This is especially true of the stunning limestone landscape, despite it being the dominant feature of the area. Although the caves have been well described in two books (see reference list), these are aimed mainly at cavers and there is very little literature to explain the surface, and underground, landscape to the ordinary visitor, other than a recent *Classic Landforms* guide by David Drew (see reference list). This book aims to plug that gap by explaining specific features of the landscape passed on the more popular routes through the Burren. To the east of the Burren the Gort lowlands form a much more subdued limestone landscape which is less frequently visited or written about. Nonetheless, it is a fascinating area which complements, and contrasts with, the Burren landscape. Anyone with an interest in the limestone landscapes of Ireland should visit the Gort area, and hence an excursion covering some of the main sites has been included here.

The sketch maps for each excursion, grouped together near the middle of this booklet, are intended only to give an indication of site locations, with not all of the roads marked. Hence visitors are strongly advised to carry larger scale maps with them. The Ordnance Survey *Discovery Series* 1:50,000 sheets 51 (most of the Burren) and 52 (the extreme eastern Burren and the Gort lowlands) cover the entire area; grid references cited in this guide are taken from those maps. Tim Robinson's *Folding Landscapes* map of the Burren is also ideal for all but the Gort excursion and has many of the sites specifically marked. Although most of the sites in this guide are adjacent to, or at least visible from, roads and tracks, many are on private land and **the wishes of the landowners and tenants must be respected**. Remember that **mention in this guide does not imply a public right of way**. Details of parking are indicated by a **P** at the end of each stop and its absence indicates that parking may be difficult. Even some of the smallest roads are in constant use so **do not block any roads**.

Although most roads within the Burren and Gort area are relatively minor, the region can be reached easily from the main centres of population. Both Galway to the north and Shannon Airport and Limerick to the south are within an hour's drive of the Burren while Dublin is only about 3 hours away. There is plentiful accommodation in the area to suit all tastes. Most of the larger hotels are around Lisdoonvarna and Ballyvaghan but there are many B&Bs scattered across the Burren and Gort region. For those on a more limited budget there are several hostels, particularly at Doolin, Roadford and Fanore. Accommodation can be in short supply during the summer months and particularly in September, during the Match-making Festival at Lisdoonvarna.

Facing directly into the Atlantic, the region experiences constantly changing weather. With an average of 260 rain days per year, fine weather is never a certainty. However, at some excursion stops there is more to see after prolonged or heavy rain. In flood some of the sinks (swallow holes) and risings (springs) can be an impressive sight while the turloughs (seasonal lakes) show a remarkable contrast between summer and winter. Coastal sites can also be spectacular during unsettled weather and the scale of some of the winter storms which hit the Burren coast almost defies belief. **Take care at all sites during or following wet weather, since the bare rocks can be very slippery. EXTREME CARE should be taken at coastal sites in even mildly unsettled conditions - never take risks with the sea.**

Some technical terms have had to be used in this book but all are explained in the next few introductory sections. To help you refer back to these explanations the technical terms have been highlighted in **colour** where they are immediately followed, or preceded, by their explanation, and there is an index of these terms at the end of the book.

Why explore the Burren and Gort area?

The Burren is one of the most distinctive and best known landscape regions in Ireland and every year is visited by many hundreds of thousands of people from all over the world. Even from the comfort of a car or coach the stark beauty, or some might call it bleakness, of the Burren, which literally means 'a rocky place', is very evident. For those venturing further from the road the Burren represents what might often seem a vast, barely explored wilderness remote from the hurly burly of modern life. Despite the huge number of visitors, the area rarely seems crowded and it is easy to find solitude whilst walking the hills or green roads. To the east the Gort lowlands appear less remote and more like other agricultural areas of Ireland. But this belies its remarkable secrets. During the summer the gently rolling landscape is dotted with shallow lakes, seemingly unconnected lengths of sluggish river emerging from vast springs before vanishing underground again, and grassy glades strewn with moss-blackened boulders. During summer the landscape sleeps, but the winter rains bring it to life again and there is a dramatic transformation. The lakes expand, the rivers become dark swirling torrents, and the grassy glades and their blackened boulders are engulfed by water pouring from beneath the ground to form temporary lakes, or turloughs.

While the uncrowded nature of the Burren and Gort lowlands is just as true of many other parts of rural Ireland, the landscape here is unique. The vast expanses of grey fissured rock rising to cliffed and terraced hills in the Burren might seem an unusual sight in a country renowned for its rolling green landscape, while the weird seasonal lakes and disappearing rivers of the Gort lowlands have an air of mystery about them. But all of these features are due to the dominant rock type in this area - limestone. Most rock types are slowly removed by mechanical erosion, usually by water breaking it into smaller particles and carrying these particles away. But limestone is different. Even though the limestone here is quite hard and resists mechanical erosion, like all limestones it has the rather peculiar property of dissolving in weakly acidic water, such as rain, to form what is called a **karst** landscape (named after a region of Slovenia where this type of landscape is well developed). Although water percolates slowly through cracks in many types of rock, only in limestone are these cracks widened by solution until eventually they are large enough to engulf all of the water which flows across the surface. For this reason karst scenery is characterised by a lack of surface drainage; instead water is channelled underground through these solutionally widened fractures. Some of them may become large enough for us to explore; we call them cave passages.

Many features of karst landscapes are typified by the Burren and the Gort lowlands and can be seen on the excursions described later in this book. Indeed, this is an internationally important karst area and the finest in Ireland. The sinking streams, springs, and fissured limestone pavements are some of the most obvious products of limestone dissolution, but dissolution is not the only process that has been important in creating the stark landscape of the Burren. During the last million years or so much of Ireland was covered several times by thick ice sheets and glaciers. The most recent glaciation, which ended only about 14,000 years ago, scraped away much of the earlier soil and shale cover to leave vast areas of bare limestone. These bare surfaces have since developed into the stunning limestone pavements for which the Burren is so famous. For this reason the Burren is often referred to as a **glaciokarst** landscape, since without the bulldozing effect of the ice sheets much of the Burren's character would not have been able to develop.

What little soil cover once remained here, or formed since the ice retreated, has largely disappeared, washed down the solutionally widened fissures. The scarcity of thick soils, and of surface water, over large areas of the Burren has profoundly influenced the plants that grow here. Indeed, Cromwell's surveyor Ludlow described the region as a "savage land, yielding neither water enough to drown a man, nor a tree to hang him, nor soil enough to bury" - an apt, if macabre, description of a classic karst landscape. But not all of the region is of bare rock. In parts of the Burren and Gort area the glaciers dumped masses of **boulder clay**, a chaotic jumble of 'ice-bulldozed' rock fragments, soil and clay. The valley floors and lower slopes of the Burren are often covered with this boulder clay, which consequently are the most intensively farmed areas. Further east boulder clay covers large areas of the Gort lowlands and has partly blocked many of the underground drainage channels which, as a result, now cause extensive flooding in winter following heavy rain.

The boundaries of the Burren and Gort lowlands

Much of the Burren is upland, typically rising to 100-150 metres in the south and about 300 metres in the north, reaching a maximum of 344 metres on the rush-covered slopes of Slieve Elva. The only significant areas of lowland, below 50 metres, within the Burren are the narrow coastal strip to the west and the valleys which extend south for several kilometres from Ballyvaghan and Bell Harbour. The physical boundaries of the Burren are fairly easy to define. To the west and north the uplands fall steeply to the coast while the eastern scarp falls just as steeply onto the adjacent Gort lowlands, which seldom rise above 30 metres. The southern margin of the Burren can be drawn where the gentle southerly dip of the limestone carries it beneath the overlying shales along an irregular line running roughly from Doolin, through Lisdoonvarna and Kilfenora, to Corofin **(see Figure 1)**.

6

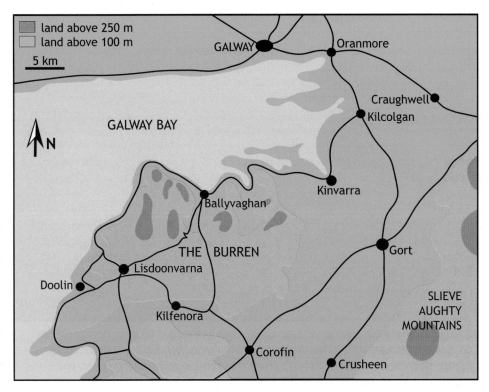

Figure 1. General map of the Burren, Gort and Galway Bay area.

Although the Burren is dominated by limestone, there are two substantial areas of the overlying shale **(see Figure 3)** that have survived erosion and extend north across the limestone beneath. These are the Knockauns Mountain and Slieve Elva ridges and, to the east, the Poulacapple ridge **(see Excursion maps 1 and 3)**. Their damp rush-covered slopes form a striking contrast with the freely draining limestone below. The boundary between the two is easily recognised by the change in vegetation and the small surface streams sinking underground on flowing from the shale onto the limestone.

The Gort lowlands to the east form a striking contrast, rarely rising more than 30 metres above sea level, but they are rather more difficult to define. Their eastern margin is defined by the foot of the Slieve Aughty Mountains while the western boundary can be drawn along the eastern scarp of the Burren uplands in the south **(see Figure 26)** and the shores of Galway Bay to the north. The northern and southern margins of the lowlands are less clear; for the purposes of this guide they are taken as far north as Craughwell and as far south as Crusheen **(see Figure 1)**.

7

Figure 2. View eastwards across Gleninagh Mountain and Ballyvaghan Bay to Moneen Mountain in the distance. The glacially rounded northern scarp of the Burren rises dramatically from a narrow coastal strip, with the terraced limestones forming the upper slopes here.

The rocks and their story

The geology of the Burren and Gort lowlands is actually very simple since there are really only two main rock types that we will see. These are the hard, grey, Carboniferous Limestone and the dark grey to black, often iron-stained, Clare Shales (**shale** is a thinly-layered mudstone) above. Both were deposited during the Carboniferous period, between about 360 and 320 million years ago. Originally they formed horizontal layers but now they dip gently southwards over most of the region; this is most obvious along the coast, with the limestone finally disappearing beneath the overlying shale near Doolin (**see Stop B1**). Although more than 450 metres of the Carboniferous Limestone are exposed on the Burren itself, the base lies several hundred metres lower still. These lower beds are occasionally seen projecting through the boulder clay on the east side of the Gort lowlands. The lowest beds seen on the Burren include dolomitic limestones (**dolomite** is a mineral composed of magnesium calcium carbonate; it is slightly less soluble than **limestone**, which is fairly pure calcium carbonate). They weather black and are seen on the lower slopes of Black Head, hence its name. Above are massive grey limestones, which form the lower slopes in the northern part of the Burren, overlain by nine thick limestone beds separated by clay bands less than a metre thick. It is these nine bands that give many of the Burren hills their distinctive terraced appearance. At the top of the limestone succession, forming the gentle slopes above the top terrace, are fossiliferous

8

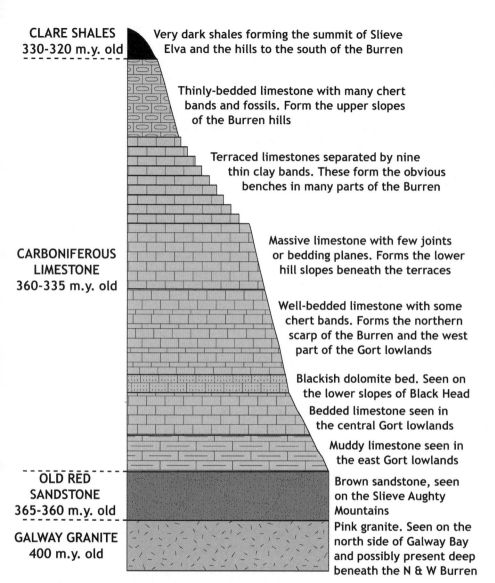

CLARE SHALES
330-320 m.y. old

Very dark shales forming the summit of Slieve Elva and the hills to the south of the Burren

Thinly-bedded limestone with many chert bands and fossils. Form the upper slopes of the Burren hills

Terraced limestones separated by nine thin clay bands. These form the obvious benches in many parts of the Burren

CARBONIFEROUS
LIMESTONE
360-335 m.y. old

Massive limestone with few joints or bedding planes. Forms the lower hill slopes beneath the terraces

Well-bedded limestone with some chert bands. Forms the northern scarp of the Burren and the west part of the Gort lowlands

Blackish dolomite bed. Seen on the lower slopes of Black Head

Bedded limestone seen in the central Gort lowlands

Muddy limestone seen in the east Gort lowlands

OLD RED
SANDSTONE
365-360 m.y. old

Brown sandstone, seen on the Slieve Aughty Mountains

GALWAY GRANITE
400 m.y. old

Pink granite. Seen on the north side of Galway Bay and possibly present deep beneath the N & W Burren

Figure 3. Vertical section through the rocks beneath the Burren and Gort lowlands (not to scale).

grey limestones with many nodules of **chert** (an impure form of flint). These are insoluble and so often protrude from weathered limestone surfaces.

Above the limestone is the other main rock type of the Burren region; the black, impermeable, Clare Shales. They outcrop on the high ground of Poulacapple and Slieve Elva, as well as to the south of the Burren limestone outcrop, and are exposed in the cliffs on the south side of Doolin Bay. Higher beds with more sandstones are superbly

9

exposed, though rather inaccessible for close inspection, in the Cliffs of Moher. All of these sandstones and mudstones were deposited in mid-Carboniferous times, about 325 million years ago. The Clare Shales are impermeable and insoluble, and hence form the catchment of many streams which then flow onto the limestone. The shales weather to an often waterlogged, heavy, grey clay which forms only poor, sedge-covered pasture. However, these thick, rather acidic soils are ideal for conifers, with which the shale cap of both Slieve Elva and Poulacapple have been extensively planted.

Other rocks, of different types and ages, come to the surface in adjacent areas but, although pieces are seldom seen here, these rocks are significant for understanding how the landscape has developed. Immediately beneath the Carboniferous Limestone are brownish sandstones and pebble beds of the Old Red Sandstone (of Devonian age, about 365 million years old). In the Burren these lie deep beneath the surface but they come to the surface in the Slieve Aughty Mountains, to the east of the Gort lowlands, where up-folded layers have been exposed as the overlying limestone has been eroded away. The Old Red Sandstone is insoluble and relatively impermeable, and so the Slieve Aughty Mountains form the main catchment for rivers draining west on to the Gort lowlands. As such they have been very important in forming the karst features found there.

To the north of our area lies the remarkably straight northern shore of Galway Bay, which is formed of Galway Granite. This formed as molten rock deep beneath the surface about 400 million years ago and almost certainly extends southwards deep beneath part of the Burren. Pebbles, and even large boulders, of Galway Granite are found scattered across the surface of the Burren and show that ice movement was from the north during the last million years or so. Still further north are the ancient (up to 750 million years old) schists, quartzites and marble of Connemara. Although having little direct bearing on the Burren landscape, these rocks from Galway and Connemara are very distinctive types which occasionally turn up as **erratics** in the debris left behind by the last glacier, providing further evidence of the direction of ice movement.

Ancient rivers, tropical seas and earth movements

The three main rock types which underlie this area, the Old Red Sandstone, Carboniferous Limestone and Clare Shales, represent enormous environmental changes over the course of about 50 million years. The sandstones and pebble beds of the Old Red Sandstone were deposited by great rivers flowing from an ancient mountain chain onto a flood plain (the hills of Connemara and Mayo to the north are perhaps the eroded stumps of some of these ancient mountains). The only fossils in these rocks, occasional small pieces of plant debris, confirm that this was land rather than sea.

But, in early Carboniferous times sea level rose and flooded across these plains. Ireland lay roughly on the Equator at that time and in the warm, tropical seas calcium carbonate was deposited to form limestone. Fossils of corals and brachiopods (a type of shellfish) show that these limestones were deposited on a shallow sea floor. At first the limestone was diluted by mud brought down by the rivers; these muddy limestones lie immediately above the Old Red Sandstone and are seen occasionally on the east side of the Gort lowlands. As sea level continued to rise, drowning more of the land, the

10

influence of these rivers became less until there was very little mud to dilute the limestone; these are the pure limestones of the rest of the Gort lowlands and of the Burren. Occasional drops in sea level exposed the limestone to rain and weathering for a few thousand years, causing its surface to become pock-marked by solution just as on the limestone pavements we see today. These ancient 'limestone pavements' are called **palaeokarst**. As sea level rose again a thin clay layer was deposited over these palaeokarst surfaces before normal limestone deposition resumed **(see Figure 20)**. The effects of these minor fluctuations in sea level are seen in the Burren terraces which have been picked out by erosion. These same clay bands can be traced across to the Aran Islands in Galway Bay and even as far as the Yorkshire Dales and the Peak District in England, so we know that they were not due to just local changes in sea level.

There is a time gap of a few million years between the highest limestone and the lowest bed of the overlying Clare Shales. Very slow deposition during this interval allowed fish teeth and scales to accumulate on the sea floor, these later being converted into phosphate minerals. These phosphate deposits are up to 2 metres thick around the village of Roadford, near Doolin, where they were once quarried for fertiliser. The sandstones and mudstones of the Clare Shales above are thought to have been deposited in deep water off the mouth of a huge river delta. Shelly fossils are common only at a few levels, notably near the base of the Clare Shales, but show that it was mostly marine. However, other animals such as marine worms or snails, whose soft bodies were never preserved as fossils, have left innumerable sinuous trails across some of the sandstones and mudstones; these are the famous Liscannor Flags which are quarried to the south of the Burren.

All of these different rocks were originally deposited in a series of unbroken horizontal layers, one upon another. But around 290 million years ago there was a period of major earth movements caused by continental plates colliding. Over much of the Burren the originally horizontal limestone beds were tilted only about 2° to the south-south-east, and there are very few faults or folds, perhaps reflecting the solid foundations provided by the Galway Granite which is thought to lie beneath much of the area. To the east and south-east the limestone is more disturbed, perhaps hinting at the limits of the buried Galway Granite. Folding is seen most spectacularly on Mullagh More, but elsewhere in the south-eastern Burren and the Gort lowlands local dips on the limestone may be quite steep.

The limestone is broken by nearly horizontal fractures formed by **bedding-planes**, which separate the original layers in which the limestone was deposited, and by vertical fractures, known as **joints**, which formed during ancient earth movements **(see Figure 4)**. The dominant joints are orientated almost north-south (196°) with a second set running east-west (270°). Their spacing, so superbly displayed on the limestone pavements **(see Figure 6)**, varies from several metres to less than a metre. Occasionally, opposing faces of some fractures are polished and bear linear grooves and ridges. These scratches are known as **slickensides** and formed as the rock surfaces moved past each other along a **fault**, which marks the epicentre of an ancient earthquake.

11

Figure 4. Bedding planes (horizontal) and joints (vertical) are clearly visible in the Carboniferous Limestone at Boodaun, on the coast near Doolin (see Stop B3). These control many of the landscape features in the Burren.

The surface landscape

The surface landscape of this area has formed through the interplay between the rocks, erosion and deposition by ice over the last million years or so, and the effects of water on the limestone and other rocks. The direct influence of geology is seen in features such as the limestone terraces, the regular fractures on the limestone pavements, and the way in which the streams flow across the shales but sink underground on reaching the limestone.

The glacial legacy

Over the past million years the entire region has been buried, probably several times, by a slowly moving ice sheet which may have been several hundred metres thick. The most recent period of ice movement ended only about 14,000 years ago. It scraped bare large areas of the limestone surface and rounded off north-facing slopes **(see Figure 2)**. Elsewhere it plucked blocks from south-facing crags and deposited chaotic masses of boulder clay in hollows and in the lee of some of the hills; these often provide the only significant soil cover on the limestone surface. As the ice moved across the landscape it gouged deep scratches, or **glacial striae**, into the rock surface beneath (unlike **slickensides** found on faults, which are sandwiched between two solid masses of rock, these glacial scratches are found only on rock surfaces or beneath boulder clay). On the bare limestone surfaces these striations have long since been dissolved away by the rain

Figure 5. Glacially striated limestone exposed as the overlying boulder clay is eroded away on the shore at Poulcraveen (Stop B4).

but those buried by boulder clay have been protected and can now be seen where it is being eroded away by the sea **(see Figure 5)**. The orientation of these glacial striations, and the presence in the boulder clay of occasional pieces of granite and other rocks from north of Galway Bay, show that the ice must have moved down across the Burren from the north-east. Limestone pavements are not found beneath areas of thick boulder clay so it is likely that many of the small-scale karst features, and at least some of the active stream sinks and caves on the Burren, probably formed since the last glacial episode. However, the larger karst landforms are too deep and extensive to have formed only in the last few thousand years. They include long and complex cave systems, such as Poulnagollum **(Stop D8)**; enormous closed depressions, such as at Carran **(Stop F6)**; and especially the Gort lowlands with its remarkable and complex subterranean drainage and network of surface lakes and turloughs **(Excursion G)**. All of these must have started to form long before the last glacial episode, perhaps even before any of the glacial activity of the last million years or so, although glacial erosion and deposition has greatly modified them since. Because of this interplay between glaciation and karstification, the karst landscape of the Burren is often referred to as **glaciokarst**. It is only through the glacial stripping of the shale and soil that once covered the limestone that the extensive limestone pavements of the Burren and Gort lowlands have been able to develop.

Solution at the surface

The small-scale features developed on bare limestone surfaces by the effects of rainfall are as diverse as the larger-scale landscape and include far more than just the familiar clints and grikes. The limestone's low porosity does not allow rainwater to soak in except along fractures. Joints are slowly widened to form a **grike**, with the adjacent block of limestone termed a **clint**. Small pools, called **kamenitzas**, may also develop on bare limestone surfaces; this is the classic form of limestone pavements **(see Figure 6)**. Clint size depends upon the joint spacing, with some clints covering many square metres in area. On sloping limestone surfaces, such as occur in parts of the south-east Burren and the Gort lowlands, rainwater drains off down slope to form sub-parallel series of runnels. Larger runnels which become deeper and wider down slope are termed **rinnenkarren**, or solution runnels **(see cover photo)**; smaller ones on steeper slopes, and with depth and width remaining fairly constant down slope, are called **rillenkarren** or solution flutes.

The retreat of the last ice sheet about 14,000 years ago left many **erratic boulders** (so called because they have been carried by the ice beyond where they are normally found) scattered across the bare limestone surface. Usually they are of limestone but sometimes of Galway Granite or other rock types. Since then rainfall has slowly lowered the limestone surface by dissolution except where it is protected by these erratics, somewhat in the manner of an umbrella. These boulders now

Figure 6. Limestone pavement on Mullagh More. Solution has picked out the vertical fractures (joints) to form the grikes (the fissures) separated by clints (the blocks in between). Rillenkarren (solution flutes) and a small kamenitza (solution pool) are visible in the foreground.

Figure 7. *This boulder at Poulsallagh (stops A4 and B12) was left behind as the last ice sheet retreated. By sheltering the limestone surface beneath from rainfall, a pedestal has developed as the exposed limestone surrounding it has been lowered by solutional weathering.*

sit on pedestals whose height, sometimes several tens of centimetres, shows the thickness of limestone that has been removed from the surrounding surface by rainfall since the ice sheets disappeared from the area **(see Figure 7)**.

Where drainage has been concentrated onto a particular point, a closed depression, known as a **doline**, may develop **(see Figure 8)**; larger, more complex examples are known as **uvalas (see Figure 25)**. Some are only a metre or two deep and a few metres across but others in the Burren, such as the Carran depression **(Stop F6)**, may have an irregular outline covering several square kilometres and up to several tens of metres deep, all reflecting a complex history of karstification and glacial modification. On the Gort lowlands, where the regional water table lies at relatively shallow depth, many of these large depressions are permanent lakes. Others are flooded only when the underground drainage system is unable to drain the water away fast enough, such as often occurs in winter; these are the **turloughs**, or 'seasonal lakes', which are such a remarkable element of the karst landscape of western Ireland. Even in summer, when they are dry, these turloughs are instantly recognisable from the presence of the Black Turlough Moss, *Cinclidotus fontinaloides*, which covers boulders, walls and bushes submerged by winter flooding **(see back cover)**.

Dry valleys are another common feature of karst landscapes where most of the drainage is underground. In the Burren permanent surface streams are found only on the

15

Figure 8. A closed depression, or doline, near Poulnabrone Dolmen (Stop E4). These are the most characteristic feature of karst landscapes; on any other rock type a depression like this would be water-filled, but on limestone the water can escape via an underground drainage route.

Clare Shales or in a few places where they flow over boulder clay, such as in the valleys of the Caher and Rathborney rivers **(stops C13 and C15)** and the floor of the Carran depression **(Stop F6)**. However, dry valleys are fairly commonplace though many have no obvious relationship to the present surface drainage. A few of the more steep-sided of these might even be termed gorges. At least some of these limestone-floored valleys and gorges probably were carved out during the cold periods of the ice age. Permafrost would have prevented summer melt water from sinking underground, which instead flowed across the surface like a normal river, excavating a valley in the process. One of the most impressive of these gorges is that which lies below Ballynalacken Castle **(Stop A2)**.

Along the coast a rather peculiar type of karst can be seen in a narrow zone directly affected by tides and waves. At low tide the limestone can be seen to be fretted into jagged or rounded pinnacles between shallow rock pools. Many of the pinnacles are encrusted with barnacles and mussels, while the large pools at low tide are crowded with purple sea urchins (*Paracentrotus lividus*) which have each excavated a small depression in which they spend their lives **(Figure 9)**. But how have these pools and pinnacles developed? They cannot have been dissolved out by sea water because this is already saturated with carbonate. Strangely, these pits and pinnacles are absent from the darkest parts of caves which have been partly drowned by the sea, such as those on Doolin Point **(Stop B2)** and at Poulsallagh **(Stop A4)**, and this is a clue to how those on the shore have

16

Figure 9. *Pinnacles and rock pools in the limestone exposed at low tide on Doolin Point (see Stop B3). Sometimes termed biokarst, they form through bioerosion by marine animals and plants, not through direct dissolution by sea water. The dark spots in the rock pool are sea urchins (Paracentrotus lividus).*

formed. In dimly lit parts of these caves the scalloped walls become increasingly broken up by sharp pinnacles which all point towards the light! This is **photokarst**, formed by microscopic algae etching the limestone in some places to leave pinnacles in others. These same algae have a similar, though less directional, effect out on the shore. Animals, such as limpets and the purple sea urchins, then graze upon the algae with their rasping tongues or teeth, while others, such as barnacles and mussels, use the pinnacles as anchor points. Together these animals and microscopic plants have created the jagged surfaces, called **biokarst**, on the shore without any direct dissolution by the sea water.

Burren uplands vs. Gort lowlands: Why so different?

Both the Burren and the Gort lowlands are made largely of the same rock type, limestone, yet the landscapes of these two regions are strikingly different. Why is this? There is no evidence that the limestone on the lowlands was weaker and more easily eroded, or that the lowlands have been gouged out by more intense ice movements. But there is evidence that the limestone has been exposed to dissolution for much longer in the Gort lowlands than over most of the Burren uplands. Beneath the irregular surface of the Burren most of the cave passages are relatively small, still actively forming, and clearly related to the present landscape. In contrast, the gently undulating Gort lowlands

17

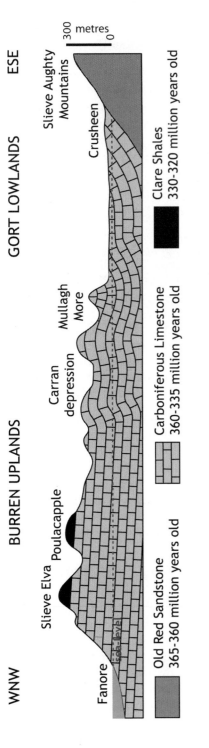

Figure 10. *East-West sketch section through the Burren and Gort lowlands, showing the relationship of the underlying rocks to the surface landscape (after P.W.Williams; see Ford and Williams 1989).*

WNW

BURREN UPLANDS

Slieve Elva
Poulacapple
Fanore
sea-level
Carran depression
Mullagh More

GORT LOWLANDS

Crusheen

Slieve Aughty Mountains

ESE

300 metres 0

Old Red Sandstone
365-360 million years old

Carboniferous Limestone
360-335 million years old

Clare Shales
330-320 million years old

are underlain by sections of enormous phreatic passage, sometimes more than 10 metres in diameter **(see Figure 27)**, connecting various surface lakes, turloughs and rivers. These cave fragments clearly represent parts of a once vast cave system now partly destroyed by surface lowering through dissolution and glacial erosion.

It is the geology that once again is the key to understanding the difference between these two areas. Many millions of years ago the limestone across the whole area would have been buried beneath a thick cover of the impermeable Clare Shales and so would have been protected from dissolution. However, because the various rock layers were upfolded in the east, across the present Slieve Aughty Mountains **(see Figure 10)**, erosion would have uncovered the limestone here first and exposed it to dissolution. Continued erosion eventually even exposed the Old Red Sandstone beneath, allowing major rivers to flow on the surface westwards onto the limestone **(see Excursion Map 4)**, where they have formed the great cave passages found beneath the Gort lowlands. Over the long term (the last few million years) the wet climate of western Ireland has actually removed limestone by dissolution faster than other rocks have been removed by erosion. On the Burren it is clear that over large areas the Clare Shales have protected the limestone beneath until relatively recently, so there has been far less time for dissolution to remove the limestone there. Indeed, a shale cap still remains on Slieve Elva and Poulacapple, and covers the limestone to the south of the Burren **(see Excursion Map 1)**, which accordingly is protected from dissolutional lowering for at least a little while longer. The distribution of hills in the Burren still reflects the irregular removal of this shale cover whereas to the east, on the Gort lowlands, the shale was eroded away so long ago that the gently folded limestone beds have been bevelled off by dissolution to form a remarkably flat 'corrosion plain'. However, the slow dissolution of the limestone which created the Gort lowlands is still operating today and ultimately, perhaps in another 2 to 3 million years, will see these lowlands extending west right across what is now the Burren!

Beneath the surface

The thick, pure limestones of the Burren and much of the Gort lowlands are ideal for the development of cave passages. However, direct rainfall onto the limestone is too dispersed to form large passages, which instead usually form where a stream flows from an impermeable catchment rock, such as shale or sandstone, onto the limestone. The point where the water passes underground is known as a **sink** (or **swallow hole**) and it finally re-emerges after its underground journey at a **rising** (or **resurgence** or **spring**).

Cave passages can develop both above the water table, in what is known as the vadose zone, or below it, in what is called the phreatic or saturated zone **(see Figure 11)**, and tend to be guided initially by pre-existing fractures such as bedding planes and joints. Phreatic caves have a passage shape which is different from that of vadose caves, and these shapes can be used to tell us where the water table was when these passages formed even long after they have dried up **(see Figure 11)**. Beneath the water table, in the **phreatic zone**, all cavities in the limestone are water-filled and so the limestone dissolves in all directions to form passages with circular or elliptical cross sections; these are often known as **phreatic tubes (see Figures 15 and 20)**. Water flow here follows the path of least resistance, even flowing uphill if necessary, like water in the U-bend under the sink. In contrast, above the water table in the **vadose zone (see Figure 11)** water flows only in the lower part of the passage and always downhill, just like a surface stream, cutting down into the floor to form a **vadose canyon (see Figure 13)**. Sometimes the stream may even drop vertically down a fault or joint to form a **vadose shaft**.

During a cave's history the water table may fall but water may continue to flow along passages that originally formed in the phreatic zone. Such passages can easily be identified by their keyhole shape, with a **vadose trench** carved into the floor of a phreatic tube **(see Figure 16)**. However, there is another type of passage, sometimes found in Burren caves, that formed in the phreatic zone yet has the appearance of a vadose canyon. These are known as **paragenetic passages** and develop where sediment (mud or sand) accumulates on the passage floor, protecting it from dissolution which instead is confined to the exposed limestone in the roof. Over time the roof slowly dissolves upwards as more sediment accumulates on the floor, producing a canyon passage largely filled with sediment. If this sediment is later washed out, the canyon shape of the passage is revealed. However, a paragenetic canyon extends *upwards* from the level at which the cave originated, such as a bedding plane, whereas a vadose canyon

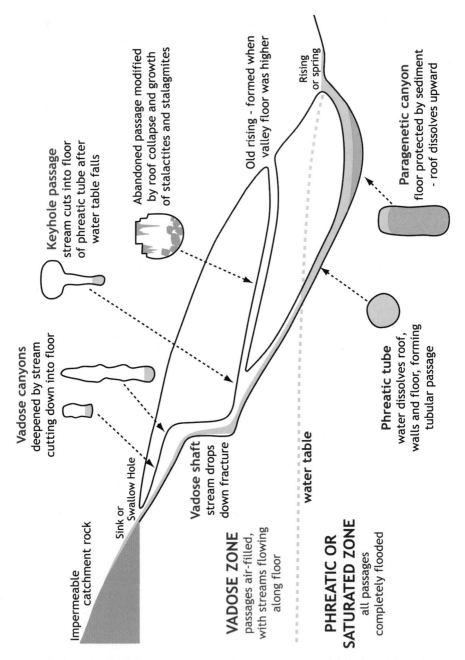

Figure 11. *Sketch section through a cave system to show the various passage shapes and their relationship to the position of the water table. Examples of all of these can be seen on the excursions.*

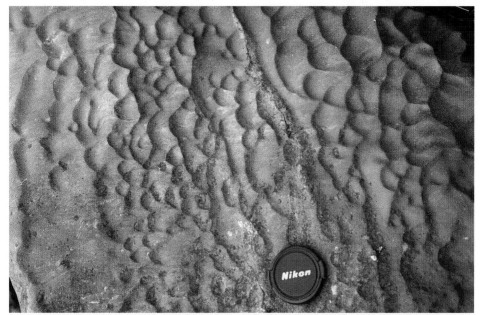

Figure 12. Solutional scalloping of a limestone surface by flowing water. These scallops (3-4 cm long) show that the water flowed from left to right at a velocity of about one metre per second (about 2 mph).

cuts *downwards* (see Figures 13 and 14). They can also be distinguished from vadose canyons by the presence of undulating ledges and notches along the walls (see Figure 17); these ledges mark the depth of sediment in the passage at various stages of its development but in vadose passages they are sub-horizontal, rather than undulating.

As well as the information which cave passage shape can tell us about the former level of the water table, it is also easy to determine the direction and speed of water flow by looking for asymmetric, scoop-shaped hollows, called **scallops** (see Figure 12). These form on passage walls by dissolution. The steeper side faces downstream and their size is determined by the speed at which the water was flowing when they formed. Small scallops indicate faster flow than larger ones and a rough rule of thumb for calculating water flow (in metres per second) is to divide 3.5 by the mean length of the scallops in centimetres. Of course, it is not always possible to recognise these various features where the passage has suffered some collapse, as is common in many larger passages and those in thinly-bedded limestones.

In section it is clear that many cave passages formed originally along bedding planes, producing wide, low, often meandering, passages (see Figure 16). Where passages were more strongly guided by vertical fractures in the limestone, straight stretches of passage are linked by right-angle bends. Although many caves in this area still carry flowing water, abandoned passages are also common. These show that many of the caves have had a long and complex history, during which they have been modified by abandonment, sediment infilling, reoccupation by flowing water and, ultimately, by

21

Figure 13. *Active vadose canyon with the stream cutting down into the floor, Doolin River Cave. The cascade entering from the roof is water leaking from the Aille River (see Stop C1), which flows above the cave near here. It marks the approximate position of the 'proto-cave' from which the present stream passage has cut downwards.*

Figure 14. *Paragenetic canyon at Oughtdarra, west of Knockauns Mountain, from which the sediment has long since been flushed out. It developed from one of the tiny 'proto caves' on the bedding plane across the middle of the picture. Sediment deposited on the passage floor confined dissolution to the roof, forming a canyon which grew upwards from the original 'proto-cave'.*

collapse and destruction. The age of the caves themselves remains poorly known though at least some must be many hundreds of thousands of years old and must have started to form when the landscape was very different from today.

Although rainwater percolating directly downwards from the bare limestone surface above rarely forms large passages, it is important in forming **stalactites**, **stalagmites** and **flowstone** which are so conspicuous in many caves. This percolation water slowly dissolves the limestone through which it passes, only to redeposit it as calcite upon entering an air-filled cavity. Hence they form only in the vadose zone. They record information on climate while the thorium-uranium isotope ratio within them can tell us how old they are and give an indication of when a phreatic passage was drained.

Figure 15. *An ancient phreatic tube abandoned by a fall in the water table and now truncated by erosion, Aillwee Mountain.*

Caves of the Burren uplands

Most of the known caves on the Burren are associated with stream sinks located along the shale edge around Slieve Elva, Knockauns Mountain **(Excursion D)** and Poulacapple. Typically these sinks lead to narrow, winding, vadose canyons with only a gentle gradient; some remain only a few metres below the surface for hundreds of metres. In others the stream may descend one or more vadose shafts, reaching a depth of more than 180 metres in one case **(see Stop C9)**. Exploration of most Burren caves has ended at flooded passages perched on the relatively impermeable chert bands in the upper beds of the limestone, even though these lie some distance above sea level. Nonetheless, the water from some caves has been traced to submarine risings a short distance off the west coast of the Burren **(see Stop B1)**.

Typical phreatic cave passages are relatively uncommon in the Burren. Most lie well away from the present shale margin and have long since been drained by a fall in the water table. The most extensive, and best known, phreatic passage in the Burren is in Aillwee Cave. It is typical of the phreatic passages known in the Burren in that it must have formed when the landscape was very different from what we see today.

For a further explanation of how caves form, and are modified subsequently, Aillwee Cave **(Stop E1)** is well worth a visit.

Figure 16. Stalactites, stalagmites and flowstone adorn Faunarooska Cave, beneath north-west Slieve Elva (Stop C10), and have been precipitated from carbonate-saturated water percolating down cracks in the rock. The original passage shape can still be seen, with a scalloped vadose trench incised into the floor of a low, wide phreatic passage formed on a bedding plane.

Caves of the Gort lowlands

The Slieve Aughty Mountains form the main catchment for the Gort lowlands, with three major rivers draining from the impermeable Old Red Sandstone uplands to disappear underground at several large sinks along the edge of the limestone lowlands to the west **(see Excursion Map 4)**. This eastern outcrop of limestone, bent up against the Slieve Aughtys, would have been exposed to rain and sinking streams long before the protective shale cover was stripped from the Burren uplands further west. Hence the Gort lowlands, and the cave passages beneath, must be very much older than most of the karst features now seen on the Burren. However, subsequent weathering and glacial erosion has destroyed large sections of this ancient cave system while glacial deposits have partially blocked many parts of the surviving underground drainage. Over large areas of the Gort lowlands today the regional water table lies very close to the surface and the karst drainage here is dominated by permanently flooded, and often very large (more than 10 metres in diameter), phreatic cave passages which drain westwards to major intertidal and submarine risings at Corranroo and Kinvarra **(Stop G12)**. Unlike most of the caves on the Burren, which can be explored easily by ordinary cavers, most of the passages beneath the Gort lowlands are permanently flooded and accessible only to divers, although there are a few notable exceptions (see Stop G4). Only a few of these flooded passages have actually been explored although some have been followed by cave divers for many hundreds of metres. They have found that the flow in some is affected by the tide, even in passages several kilometres inland!

A major investigation of the karst drainage of the area was undertaken following severe floods in 1995 and, by using dyes and other markers to trace the flow of water between sinks and risings, we now know a lot more about the underground drainage patterns. But until cave divers actually explore all of the passages we can do no more than guess about the exact route the water takes. Hence the straight dotted lines on Excursion Map 4 are there only to show which sinks and risings have been proven (by dye tracing) to be connected; the precise route the water takes undoubtedly is far more complex.

Drainage through these often sediment choked passages is rather poor and this often leads to temporary flooding of low areas on the surface above. These are the turloughs, or seasonal lakes, for which this area is famed. For further information on the workings of turloughs the Visitor Centre at Coole Park (Stop G7), near Gort, is well worth a visit.

EXCURSION MAPS

These four sketch maps provide only an indication of the routes to be followed for the seven excursions, A to G, described in the following section. It is recommended that more detailed maps are also consulted. Details of parking, where possible, are indicated by a **P** at the end of each site description.

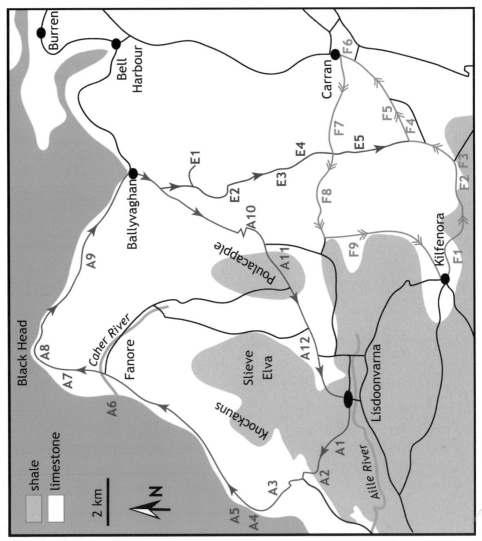

Map1. *Sketch map for the main cycling and driving tours of the Burren (Excursions A, E and F).*

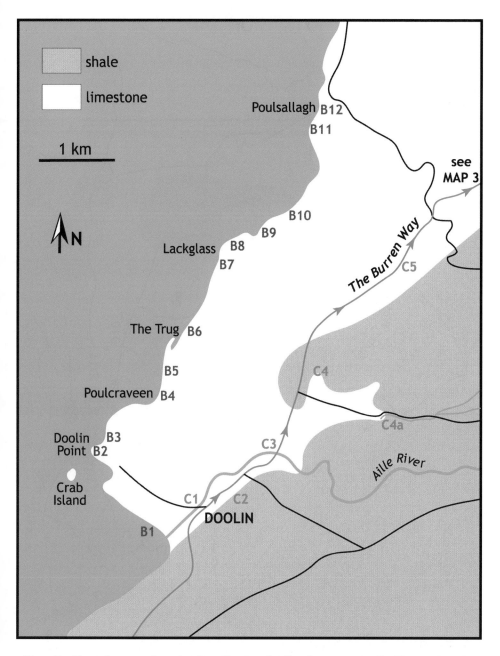

Map 2. Sketch map for the Doolin-Poulsallagh coast walk (Excursion B) and the southern part of the Burren Way (Excursion C).

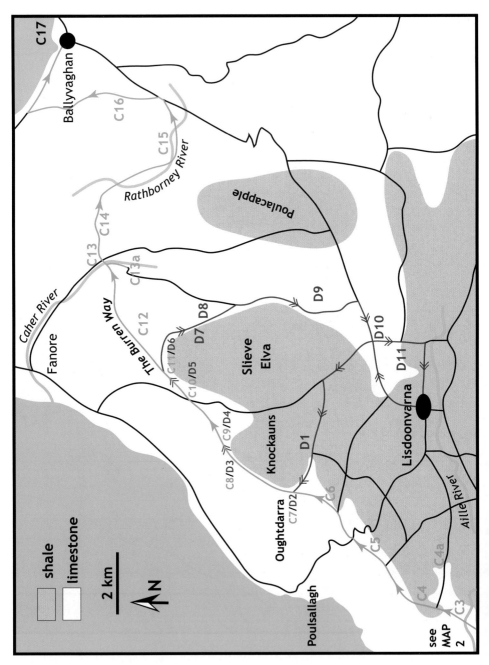

Map 3. Sketch map for the northern part of the Burren Way (Excursion C) and the Slieve Elva Circuit (Excursion D).

28

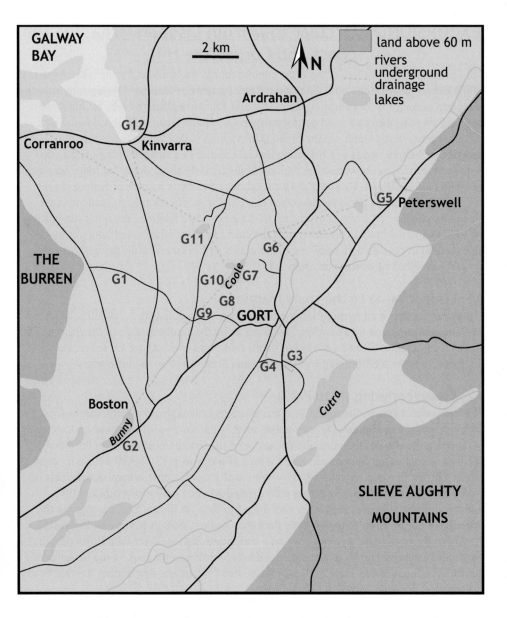

Map 4. Sketch map of sites in the Gort lowlands (Excursion G).

EXCURSIONS

EXCURSION A. Circular tour from Lisdoonvarna, via the coast and Corkscrew Hill.

This excursion follows one of the most popular tourist trails and is a route taken by many of the Burren coach tours operating out of Lisdoonvarna or Galway. Descending from the shale cap around Lisdoonvarna it passes through a heavily glaciated area of limestone before following the coast road northwards, around Black Head to Ballyvaghan. From there the route heads south, up the broad Ballyvaghan valley before ascending the spectacular hairpin bends of Corkscrew Hill and thence onto the shale cap once again. Some of the sites can be viewed in passing or justify only short stops, but more time can be spent at Poulsallagh, Fanore and Murroogh where there is a range of features to see.

The overall excursion is described in a clockwise direction from Lisdoonvarna since this affords better views of several of the large-scale features, though it can easily be followed in the reverse direction as is the case for many of the coach tours. It makes an excellent cycle ride with only one major climb, at Corkscrew Hill, though there are several long gradual inclines en route.

A1. Lisdoonvarna to the shale margin

For about the first 4 km west of Lisdoonvarna the road is across the undulating outcrop of Clare Shales which lie above the limestone along the southern edge of the Burren. The shales form a rather bleak landscape of damp acidic soils with abundant sedge, very different from the well-drained soils and famous flora found on the limestones.

A2. Craggycorradan (R 103997)

Stopping, with care, by the roadside at this sharp right-hand bend affords spectacular views across the landscape. Directly to the north is the tower of Ballynalackan Castle, perched on the edge of the normally dry gorge of the lower Coolagh River. Further sections of this gorge can be seen to the west and north-west (**Stop C5**) before it peters out in a broad flat area, criss-crossed by stone walls, as the coast is approached. This dry valley may have been formed during glacial periods when permafrost blocked the undergound drainage and meltwater was forced to flow on the surface, carving out this impressive gorge. Even today extreme floods cause the Coolagh River sink (**Stop D1**), 1.5 km to the north-east, to overflow and a continuous surface river then flows past the castle and has been known to flood the road here. Further to the east, in the background, can be seen the rounded shale outlier of Knockauns Mountain, descending westwards to the terraced limestone crags of Oughtdarra.

P - there is only very limited space for parking at the roadside here.

A3. Ballynalackan to Poulsallagh

Descending from the Ballynalackan cross-roads there are fine views of the rounded shale mass of Knockauns and the glacially plucked crags and terraces of Oughtdarra. Further

30

down the road winds through chaotic heaps of glacial debris, now thickly clothed with thorn and hazel scrub and scattered with massive limestone erratics left by the retreating ice sheets.

A4. Poulsallagh (M 085017)

It is worth stopping to look around this small but fascinating bay. Features on the south side of the bay are described for **Stop B12**. To the north of the bay is an extensive area of limestone pavement with typical Burren flora. Limestone erratics lie scattered across the surface, with some perched on conspicuous pedestals left as the limestone surface around has been lowered by dissolution **(see Figure 7)**. There are also two very interesting fragments of cave passage here. The crag immediately north of the boulder beach is pierced by Poulsallagh cave itself. At low tide and in calm weather the first part of the passage can be entered for a short distance (it has been followed northwards for several tens of metres, meandering past two roof openings, to a boulder blockage). Although the passage has the tall, narrow appearance of a vadose canyon, the undulating notches and ledges on the walls (visible even in the unroofed seaward end of the passage) show that it actually formed *below* the water table by paragenesis.

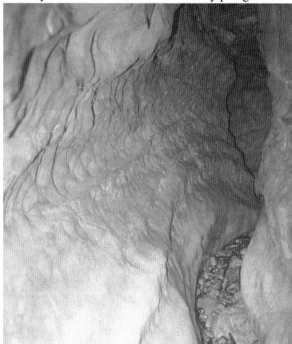

Figure 17. Paragenetic canyon in Poulsallagh Cave (Stop A4). The undulating ledges on the walls are typical of this type of cave and distinguish it from a vadose canyon, where similar ledges always slope downstream or are nearly horizontal. Note the conspicuous scalloping of the walls, which indicates the direction and speed of water flow (see Figure 12).

Little more than 100 metres to the north-east is the largely unroofed remnant of another ancient cave passage cutting inland from the cliff. The roof survives at the landward end which still contains some of the original sediments. These are remarkable for the great abundance of quartz pebbles they contain (quartz is a very rare mineral on the Burren, though common in many other places), but there are also pebbles of Galway granite and

31

Connemara schists showing that the material came from the north side of Galway Bay. Ice must have carried the pebbles to this area and later they were swept into the cave by streams eroding the boulder clay. However, granite and quartz are quite rare in the boulder clay found on the surface of the Burren today, even that on the south side of this small bay, which instead is mostly full of pieces of limestone. This suggests that these quartz-rich deposits came from an older boulder clay which was swept away by the most recent glaciation.

P - there are two good parking areas on the landward side of the road just north of Poulsallagh Bay.

A5. Mirror Wall (M 089029)

Less than a kilometre further north along the road a conspicuous dry stone wall extends west from the road. From here it is a short walk to the edge of Mirror Wall, though **take care since the cliff falls sheer into the sea**. Popular with climbers, this strikingly smooth cliff more than 30 metres high has developed as cliff falls have exposed a major north-south joint surface.

P - there is space for parking just to the south of the drystone wall on the landward side of the road.

A6. Fanore beach (M 137082)

Walk west from the car park to the broad sandy beach fronting the dune system. Where the Caher River enters the sea the pebbles at its mouth are coated with a creamy-white crust of calcite deposited by the river, which further upstream flows across boulder clay rich in calcium carbonate. In places the dunes, and sometimes the beach sand, have been stripped back to reveal an ancient limestone pavement, with the grikes often filled with cemented sands. Further north along the beach the south-facing flanks of limestone ledges and boulders have been faceted and polished by sand blown against them by the prevailing south-westerly winds **(see Figure 18)**.

P - there is an obvious car park on the landward side of the dunes.

A7. Murroogh (M 146107)

Between the road and the shore here there is an extensive area of limestone pavement. Fine examples of clints, grikes, kamenitzas and other features can be seen here, and the pavements and small crags support a profusion of typical Burren plants. There are some particularly fine examples of boulders perched on pedestals quite close to the road. The boulders have acted like umbrellas, protecting the limestone beneath them from dissolution by the rain **(see Figure 7)**.

P - there is space for a few cars by the roadside on the conspicuous bend north of Murroogh.

A8. Black Head (M 154122)

Black Head probably takes its name from the dark colour which develops on weathered dolomite, with a thick bed of this rock type being exposed in the lower slopes here. In the

32

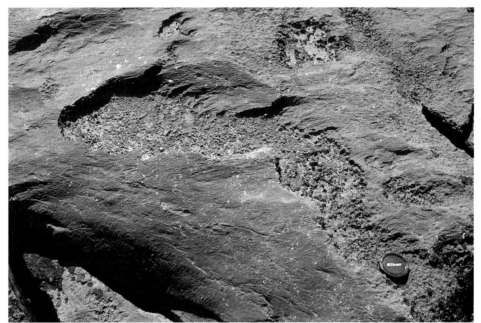

Figure 18. Kamenitzas (solution pans) modified by sand-blasting on the shore at Fanore (Stop A6). Limestone facing into the prevailing south-west winds (left to right on this picture) is polished and rounded by wind-blown sand.

dolomite crags on the landward side of the road near the lighthouse are a series of small cave fragments spread over a 200 metre length of cliff. They appear to be relics of an ancient phreatic cave system long since truncated by glacial and marine erosion.

To the east of Black Head the hills plunge steeply to the sea from a height of more than 250 metres, with the entire northward-facing scarp smoothed and rounded by the southward movement of ice more than 14,000 years ago.

P - there is only very limited parking space near Black Head lighthouse.

A9. Pinnacle Well, Tobercornan (M 201097)

A small, gothic-style shelter has been built over the limestone pavement where water emerges from a small spring. The output from this spring changes little throughout the year or even after heavy rain, indicating that the water is derived from slow and diffuse percolation into the limestone rather than from a discrete stream sink.

P - there is ample parking on either side of the holy well.

A10. Corkscrew Hill (M 206027)

The viewpoint near the top of Corkscrew Hill affords spectacular views northwards along the Ballyvaghan valley and adjacent hills. On the east side of the valley is a series of hills diminishing in height to the north (Aillwee, Moneen Mountain, Ballyconreag and, across the inlet to Poulaclogh Bay, Knockvorneen). Immediately west of the

33

viewpoint is Poulacapple, with its sedge-covered shale cap and limestone beneath covered with vegetated boulder clay. It extends north to the Rathborney River, beyond which rises Cappanawalla, with its lower slopes draped with grassed-over boulder clay. The plateau south of Corkscrew Hill is a vast area of limestone pavement, often dominated by hazel and thorn scrub and interspersed with dry-stone walls and patches of rough pasture.

The Ballyvaghan Valley, and the Turlough Valley to the east, are very old features of the Burren. They may have formed by streams draining northwards onto the limestone when the shale cap above extended right up to the northern scarp of the Burren. At that time the low corrosion plain of the Gort lowlands probably extended well out into what is now Galway Bay. But the shale cover has long since been stripped away and marine erosion has slowly eaten eastwards into the Gort lowlands. It shows the difficulties of trying to interpret a landscape where much of the evidence has been destroyed.

P - there is ample parking at the viewpoint.

A11. Doonyvardan (M 198019)

Just beyond the minor road south to Kilfenora, at Doonyvardan, there is an abrupt steepening of the slope and change in vegetation to sedge and conifer plantations. This marks the boundary between the limestone and the overlying Clare Shales of Poulacapple.

A12. South-east Slieve Elva

Emerging from the conifer plantations of Poulacapple, the road descends gently onto the limestone again with patches of limestone pavement interspersed with grassed over boulder clay. Across the valley to the north-west lies the steep eastern scarp of Slieve Elva, beneath which lies the Poulnagollum cave system, the longest in Ireland with more than 14 km of explored passages **(see Excursion D)**.

A13. Lisdoonvarna

Continuing the gentle descent into Lisdoonvarna the road passes back onto the shale outcrop, giving way to a landscape of rounded, sedge-covered drumlins. The small town of Lisdoonvarna became a spa town in 1845 on the basis of several small springs, each with a distinct chemistry which was supposed to confer medicinal properties. Of these, the Iron Well, Magnesia Well and Sulphur Well are still exploited on a small scale and are worth tasting. All of these springs emerge from the Clare Shales above the limestone. Although the shale supposedly is an impermeable rock, numerous fractures within it allow enough groundwater movement to feed these springs. Decomposition of the mineral iron pyrite (iron sulphide) and other minerals within the shales have produced the distinctive chemistry of the water.

P - there is ample parking in the town.

EXCURSION B: The coast from Doolin to Poulsallagh

Traversing the coast northwards from Doolin to Poulsallagh **(see Excursion Map 2)** is a splendid walk in itself but also provides an ideal opportunity to observe the 'anatomy' of the upper part of the limestone succession. Bedding planes, joints and faults are all picked out in detail by marine weathering, while the peculiar coastal karst forms are spectacularly displayed at low tide. The scale of the storm beaches, littered with limestone blocks plucked from the cliffs and shore, testify to the awesome power of some of the storms which strike this Atlantic coast.

This excursion can be traversed only on foot, with the full walk (one way) taking 3-4 hours. Though the terrain is rather uneven in places, there are no major climbs to negotiate. **Great care should be taken on this walk since the terrain is quite rough in places and there are certain sections where the cliffs fall sheer into the sea. It is inadvisable to attempt the walk during stormy weather. P - there is ample parking at either end of the walk, at Doolin Quay and Poulsallagh (see stop A4).**

B1. Doolin Strand (R 065963)

Fisherstreet Bay forms the extreme south-west corner of the Burren. The ledges on its north side are very near the top of the Carboniferous Limestone but, dipping gently southwards, they soon descend below the Clare Shales which form the dark cliffs on the south side of the bay stretching south-westwards to the Cliffs of Moher and beyond. The Aille River reaches the sea near the centre of the bay only in flood; normally it sinks into its bed further upstream **(see Stop C1)** to enter the Doolin River Cave. Water from the cave may well up through the sand near the mouth of the Aille River, or from bedding planes in the limestone just to the north, but most emerges from the sea bed about 100 metres offshore.

B2. Doolin Point and Hell (R 056974)

Near the seaward end of Doolin Point lies a spectacular, partly unroofed, vadose cave passage, known locally as 'Hell', developed on a major north-south joint. It descends below sea level to the north and must have formed when sea level was lower. Remnants of four small phreatic tubes emerge from the bedding plane at the foot of the crag to the east and meander towards Hell. **Only experienced cavers or climbers should attempt to descend into Hell, and even then only at low tide and in calm weather.** In the darker reaches of the cave the original solutional scalloping, formed when the cave carried an active stream, can still be seen. However, as the unroofed section is approached the scallops become increasingly dissected by small pinnacles and ridges, up to several centimetres long, which are orientated towards the light. These **photokarren** form by the etching action of endolithic blue-green algae (living just below the surface of the rock) and have a predominantly grey-green colour in more dimly lit parts of the cave but are a striking red colour where more strongly lit. Similar features can be seen around the entrance of Poulsallagh Cave **(Stop A4)** where they are more accessible.

B3. Boodaun (R 057976)

In this small bay, just to the north of Doolin Point, the vertical joints and horizontal bedding planes of the limestone are very evident where they have been picked out by marine weathering (see Figure 4). The strikingly stepped form of the coast here also demonstrates how the Burren coast is being eroded by the sea, with blocks plucked by the waves and thrown inland to form the spectacular storm beach behind. Patches of boulder clay with striated boulders can be found resting on the glacially striated limestone surface in places immediately behind this storm beach.

A major cave passage, Mermaid's Hole, emerges at Boodaun some 15 metres below sea level and is associated with several blow holes on the platform above. It has been followed inland for almost a kilometre and is just part of a whole complex of drowned cave passages which lie beneath Doolin Point and Boodaun, of which only Hell is accessible to non-divers.

Continue northwards towards Poulcraveen over southward-dipping ledges backed by a storm-beach of massive boulders. The limestone here, and for some distance north, contains many irregular bands of chert which, being insoluble, weather out as knobbly black layers. The silica of which the chert is made was derived from countless sponge spicules and microscopic radiolaria which lived in the tropical Carboniferous sea.

The ledges exposed at low tide all along this stretch of coast have been etched by a variety of, often microscopic, marine organisms into a fantastic array of irregular pinnacles and pools encrusted with barnacles and mussels. The floors of the largest, and lowest, of these pools are studded with spiny sea urchins (*Paracentrotus lividus*), each of which occupies its own made-to-measure hollow (see Figure 9).

B4. Poulcraveen (R 064981)

Approaching Poulcraveen Bay from the south, the storm beach of large angular limestone blocks plucked from the cliffs gives way towards the back of the bay to more rounded boulders which have come from erosion of the adjacent boulder clay. Although most are also of limestone, there are also boulders of pale brown sandstone and occasional black limestone nodules packed with spirally-coiled shells of fossil goniatites, a distant, and long extinct, relative of the squid. Both are from the Clare Shales and show that the ice travelled across the shale to reach this point.

The bay is backed by an irregular cliff, in places buried beneath boulder clay. There are several short sections of cave passage in this cliff which obviously have been truncated by glacial erosion and so must be older than the last ice advance. With care, the largest can be traversed at low tide although the boulders here are very slippery. The shape of these passages is very like typical vadose canyons, formed above the water table, but several clues show that they are actually paragenetic canyons formed below the water table. Firstly, small tributary passages actually join the main passage quite low on the wall, indicating that the roof level has risen since the passages first formed. Secondly, towards the northern end of the cliff there is a prominent arch, representing a remnant of cave roof, which lies about 2 metres above a bedding plane with many small tubes or 'proto caves', again showing that the roof level has risen. In a vadose canyon the 'proto

Figure 19. Looking out from the ancient paragenetic canyon at Poulcraveen (Stop B4), which has been truncated by glacial and marine erosion.

caves' and the roof of each tributary passage would be at the same level as the roof of the main passage.

To the north of the main cliff the limestone surface beneath the boulder clay shows striking glacial striations with a north-east to south-west orientation **(see Figure 5)**.

B5. From Poulcraveen to The Trug (R 066986)

Beyond the bay of Poulcraveen, a series of broad stepped coastal platforms can be followed northwards, rising gently up with the dip of the limestone over a distance of several hundred metres before the coast swings round eastwards to a sheer, north-south, joint-aligned cliff plunging some 30 metres to the sea. The limestone platform immediately to the south is breached by The Trug, a spectacular deep and narrow gully extending almost 100 metres southwards from the cliff edge. This has developed along a minor fault, the limestone on the west side having been downthrown by about 1.5 metres. This fault can be followed, sometimes as a prominent step, in other places as a boulder-choked gully, for several hundred metres further south to where it becomes buried beneath the storm beach.

At the foot of the terrace immediately landward of this small fault scarp a prominent bedding plane is riddled with innumerable small anastamosing tubes ('proto-caves') and a few larger phreatic half tubes up to a metre or so across. The larger tubes have large scallops indicating rather slow water flow down-dip to the south; like the passages at Poulcraveen, with which these tubes may once have been linked, they formed when the water table was higher in an environment very different from that of the present coast.

B6. North from The Trug

On reaching the southern end of The Trug ascend eastwards to the next main terrace, which is backed by a prominent storm beach of plucked limestone blocks and more rounded cobbles reworked from the boulder clay. Immediately behind is a two metre high face of orange-brown boulder clay with rounded cobbles of limestone and occasionally sandstone. This rests on a strikingly smooth limestone surface with clear NNE-SSW glacial striations, but these have been erased by recent dissolution only a short distance in front of the present limit of the boulder clay.

B7. Lackglass (R 072995)

At the northern end of the sheer cliff described at **Stop B5**, a stepped descent can be made to reach intertidal ledges at Lackglass. Here, where the cliff swings inland into a shallow gully eroded along a WSW-ENE fracture, the shore is strewn with house-sized boulders plucked from the cliff; their huge size reflects the presence of a particularly massive bed of limestone, almost 10 metres thick, in the lower part of the cliff. The intertidal ledge here is scarred with a striking series of parallel grooves and ridges orientated almost north-south and which can be traced across the entire outcrop of this bedding plane for several hundred metres northwards; more of these striations can be seen on the next major bedding plane some 10 metres higher, while the metre-thick limestone bed above is particularly rich in the shells of fossil brachiopods. These striations can be traced into the cliff and clearly are different from the glacial striations seen on many rock surfaces elsewhere. They are called **slickensides** and form when two masses of rock move past each other during earthquakes. Their presence on these bedding planes shows that ancient earth movements caused some of the limestone beds in the Burren to slide across those below.

At low tide the intertidal ledge can be followed southwards, down-dip around the headland into two other fracture-guided gullies. The headland itself is pierced by a network of small phreatic tubes which have developed along the fault plane. They can be negotiated by small adults but **it should be remembered that these small and constricted passages are completely flooded by the incoming tide.**

The slickensided intertidal ledge can be followed up-dip to the north and becomes narrower as a white-dappled crag, formed on a joint-aligned calcite vein, is approached. Two phreatic half-tubes in this crag are developed on the slickensided bedding plane. One can be followed (crawling only!) for some 40 metres north-eastwards to a blockage of boulders and sand washed in from a surface choke.

It is necessary now to retrace ones steps southwards to the shallow gully before ascending to the top of the cliff and continuing northwards once more. This passes over a massive sea cave at the back of a shallow bay. A shallow boulder-choked depression in the fretted limestone pavement just inland from the southern corner of this bay marks the point of collapse into the small cave passage mentioned in the previous paragraph. A little further north the joints several metres inland from the cliff edge have started to gape as the sea cave beneath undermines the cliff; not a place for the faint-hearted.

B8. North from Lackglass

Just to the north of the sea cave there is an easy descent back onto the slickensided bedding plane. Negotiating a small area of giant boulders strewn across the cliff top, descend at any convenient and safe spot on to the next major terrace below. Another

Figure 20. Ancient phreatic half-tube, north of Lackglass (Stop B8). This has developed above a much older limestone pavement, or palaeokarst surface, pitted with hollows. One of these hollows, filled with iron-stained greenish shale, is beneath the undercut to the left of the cave entrance.

'tongue' of monumental boulders extends across this terrace to the north but stop to inspect the small crag just to the south of this point. The lowest half metre or so is composed of very rubbly limestone while the surface on which it rests is pitted with deep hollows. These features represent a palaeokarst surface, the ancient equivalent of the modern limestone pavement but formed during the early Carboniferous, some 340 million years ago, when sea level dropped briefly to expose the limestone to the weather.

Just to the north of this 'tongue' of boulders an obvious phreatic cave passage, about a metre across, lies at the foot of the crag. It appears to have formed immediately above an impervious shale band associated with the ancient palaeokarst surface **(Figure 20)**. Fossil brachiopod shells are abundant on the limestone surfaces nearby.

B9. Glasha More Bay (M 077002)

Either remain on the palaeokarst surface and ascend to the north or else descend to a lower terrace and then reascend as the small cliffed bay of Glasha More is approached, skirting around it to the east. Numerous large limestone erratic boulders, often with a yellow cap of the lichen *Xanthoria*, lie scattered across the hillside in this area, looking like the giant stone heads of Easter Island.

Glasha More is a small narrow bay developed at the foot of a small dry valley. The beach is of large limestone cobbles but there are also numerous fragments of creamy flowstone and tufa. These have been broken off deposits left by percolation springs in the higher part of the bay. The dry valley can be followed inland between low crags to end where it intercepts a north-south trending grassy linear depression some 2 to 3 metres wide. This feature can be traced for hundreds of metres to the south but it should be followed northwards, down the hill to a narrow steep-sided inlet. This, and the linear feature just descended, have developed along a minor fault, with calcite veining clearly visible where erosion has removed the soil cover on the cliff top.

B10. North from Glasha More

Northwards from the minor gully just described, the cliffs become lower and the coast is dominated by massive storm beaches. Thin patches of boulder clay and smoothed, rounded areas of limestone testify to the effects of glacial erosion and deposition. A 'natural bridge' parallel to the cliff edge has formed some 800 metres north of Glasha More as a result of marine erosion plucking blocks from between the north-south joints in the limestone.

This section of the coast affords splendid views north-eastwards to the limestone crags and terraces of Oughtdarra, tailing off towards the coast, and the shale cap of Knockauns Mountain rising to the east.

B11. Cancapple (M 084014)

The boulder storm beach here, derived from plucking of the limestone outcrops, is backed by a lower beach of much smaller, well-rounded cobbles derived from erosion of boulder clay. These cobbles are mostly of limestone and pale brown sandstone, the latter from the Clare Shales. Occasional more exotic lithologies include pieces of Galway granite and Connemara schists which have been transported as much as 50 km south by ice more than 14,000 years ago.

B12. Poulsallagh Bay (M 085017)

The last ice sheet in this area moved south-eastwards to produce the glacially rounded and striated rock faces on the south side of the bay and the more angular plucked crags on the north side, while at the same time leaving a chaotic mass of broken-up rock debris as the boulder-strewn landscape immediately inland. Glacial striations, with a general northeast-southwest orientation, are superbly exposed on the south side of the bay beneath a cover of boulder clay composed largely of limestone fragments and finely-powdered limestone. However, the limestone below this boulder clay is cut by a half-metre wide, north-south orientated fissure filled with a different, and older, boulder clay which contains numerous pieces of granite and quartz. Being lodged in this fissure it has survived the more recent glaciations which destroyed virtually all trace of this older boulder clay on the surface.

There are several interesting things to see on the north side of the bay, and these are described in **Stop A4**. They are best reached by skirting behind the massive storm beach which occupies the centre of the bay.

Excursion C. The Burren Way

The Burren Way extends from Lahinch in the south to Ballyvaghan in the north, a distance of 45 km of fairly easy walking, though with a few hills (**Excursion Maps 2 and 3**). Until Doolin is reached the route is entirely on the Clare Shales and sandstones above, but thereafter it lies entirely on the limestone beneath. Although karst features can be seen in profusion along the route, those worthy of specific mention occur only sporadically, with a particular concentration on the section between Ballynalacken and the Caher Valley. Although some parts of the Burren Way are along metalled roads, and hence accessible to ordinary motor vehicles, the higher parts of the route are on rough tracks which can be negotiated only on foot or with a robust bicycle. The route is described from south to north.

C1. Doolin

The Burren Way descends into Doolin from the steep slopes of Clare Shales and sandstones immediately to the south. The Aille River at this point flows on the very top of the limestone and in summer may be dry for a considerable stretch, with all of the water sinking to flow through the Doolin River Cave only a few metres below the surface (**see Figure 13**). Most of the water re-emerges from a submarine spring about 100 metres offshore from the mouth of the Aille River, although in wet weather water may also well up through the sand on the beach and from fissures in the limestone ledges just to the north.

P - there is parking alongside the road downstream of the bridge.

C2. Fisherstreet Pot (R 075967)

A rather inconspicuous clump of scrubby trees in the field just a few metres north-east of the Doolin Activity Lodge marks the top of a 12 metre deep pothole which drops into the lower end of the Doolin River Cave. The upper half of the shaft is in the Clare Shales but no surface stream flows into it, showing that it has formed by collapse from below rather than as a stream sink.

C3. Roadford Bridge (R 080973)

The Aille River at this point lies upstream of the sinks which drain into Doolin River Cave. Consequently the river here will be flowing even if it is dry at Doolin.

P - there is parking at several places within a short distance of the bridge.

C4. Aran View Swallet (R 085983) and Doolin Road Sink (R 094978)

A small stream sinks in the field just below and to the east of Aran View. This is Aran View Swallet, one of the main entry points to the 10 km long Doolin River Cave. The passage between the sink and the main cave passes directly beneath the cemetery! Fisherstreet Pot (**Stop C2**), the lowest point of entry to the Doolin River Cave system, lies some 2 km to the south-west from here. A kilometre to the east is the more spectacular Doolin Road Sink (**Stop C4a**). The stream sinking into the limestone at the foot of the shale slope here is the largest to enter the Doolin River Cave system.

41

C5. Craggycorradan (R 097997)

Cliffs on either side of the road mark the edges of a major dry valley which can be traced north-eastwards, past Ballynalackan Castle (see Stop A2), to the Coolagh River sink (see Stop D1). Although probably formed by surface meltwater when the underground drainage routes were blocked by permafrost, a low grassy drumlin on the floor just east of the road shows that the valley must be older than the last glacial advance which left this heap of boulder clay. Beneath the south cliff on the east side of the road is Pol an Ionain, a small cave famed for its remarkable stalactite more than 6.5 metres long.

C6. Cloghaun dolines (M 110008)

About a kilometre beyond the Ballynalacken crossroads is a large grassy closed depression just east of the road and a more elongate one just to the west. They perhaps formed as stream sinks, since abandoned by retreat of the shale edge.

C7 (D2) Oughtdarra (M 114018)

From the road junction here there are spectacular views across the crags and terraces of Oughtdarra. Ice moving from the north-east plucked blocks from the south-facing slopes and left countless erratic boulders and heaps of boulder clay strewn across the terraces below. Several small, but interesting, caves now exposed in the crags (see Figure 14) obviously pre-date the last glaciation but all are notoriously difficult to find

C8. (D3) Poulnagree (M 121034)

A large concrete tank and nearby cattle trough 30 metres west of the track are useful landmarks for this pothole, which lies just to the south. An easy descent in the south-west corner affords views into a steeply descending passage, aligned along a north-south joint, leading to 2 km of vadose streamway. Poulnagree lies well away from the shale margin on the edge of a broad limestone platform overlooking a more dissected area of limestone hollows and crags. It is an old sink now largely abandoned since the shale margin was eroded to its present position by the last glaciation. Several hollows at the shale edge east of the track mark the position of the modern sinks for this cave system.

C9. (D4) Balliny Depression (M 132038)

A shallow, north-facing, embayment has been eroded into the shale edge between the northern end of Knockauns Mountain and the shale ridge of Slieve Elva to the east. To the north the limestone surface is broken by several closed depressions of which the largest is the Balliny Depression. This is a typical uvala, with an irregular shape, steep limestone walls up to 10 metres high and a gently undulating grassy floor. It is a fairly ancient feature, thought to have formed where several streams draining from the surrounding shale slopes converged. Two gullies diverge from the northern end of the depression; one extends north-north-east for several hundred metres while the other, rather less distinct, extends east-north-east. A third gully extends down the hillside from the west side of the uvala and is thought to have formed as a flood overflow. There are several minor sinks in the floor of the uvala, either adjacent to the shale margin or fed by

42

water draining off patches of boulder clay. Two important caves lie beneath the Balliny Depression. Pollballiny is more than 2 km long and contains one of the largest passages in the Burren, some 3 metres wide and up to 25 metres high. The other, Poll na gCéim, is less than 900 metres long but, at 181 metres deep, is the second deepest cave in Ireland.

C10. (D5) Kilmoon-Fanore Road & North-west Slieve Elva (M 137046)

North from Balliny the Burren Way crosses a minor metalled road for a short distance before another rough track bears off to the right along the north-west flank of Slieve Elva. A large boulder of Galway Granite, with conspicuous pink crystals of the mineral feldspar, has been built into the base of the wall only about 5 metres north of the stone way-marker near the start of this section of track. It has been carried by ice nearly 20 km from the north side of Galway Bay.

Along the first stretch of track the sedge-covered shale cap can be seen on the skyline to the east. The inconspicuous entrance of Faunarooska Cave (see Figure 16) lies at the foot of the shale scarp, with the passage passing beneath the track in this area. To the west are fine views of the coast, with the straight edge of the granite outcrop visible on the north side of Galway Bay, the sand dunes of Fanore in the foreground and, to the south-west, the Aran Islands stretching out westwards into the Atlantic.

P - there is space for parking several cars on the metalled stretch of road.

C11. (D6) Tobar an Athar Calbach holy well (M 151053)

The track continues to rise gently, passing a ruined stone cottage shortly before a fainter track bears off to the east. Follow this, past a very uneven landscape of limestone crags and hollows just to the south, to reach a strikingly flat limestone platform extending out from the foot of the shale slope. A small cross marks the site of the Holy Well. This is actually a short unroofed section of minor vadose stream cave, fed by a stream sinking 50 metres to the east in a small hollow marked by a Goat Willow bush. A little west of the Holy Well a small scar exposes the dark grey Clare Shales, while just beyond is another stream sink; a scrub filled hollow with the sound of falling water. Not far to the south-west the flat limestone terrace ends abruptly at the edge of a crag overlooking a much more irregular landscape of crags, gullies and closed depressions, a stark contrast to the flat surface at the foot of the shale slope (see Figure 21). It is thought that this flat platform represents limestone concealed by shale until the last glaciation, and hence modified by only about 14,000 years of karstification, while the more dissected landscape further out had its shale cover stripped some time earlier, perhaps in the previous glaciation. The floor of the large irregular closed depression at the southern end of this area is pocked with smaller depressions; one on the west side is a 26 metre deep vadose shaft in which falling water can be heard. Great swathes of Mountain Aven (*Dryas octopetalla*), a Burren flora speciality, are found in this area.

Continue westwards to rejoin the Burren Way. Alternatively, follow the gully northwards to rejoin the track heading east. This forms part of the Slieve Elva Circuit (Excursion D) and skirts around the shale edge, past many small sedge-covered hollows, before swinging south-east along the eastern flank of Slieve Elva.

Figure 21. Looking north-east along the north-west flank of Slieve Elva (Stop C11/D6). The terrace on the skyline is where the shale cover was stripped by the last glaciation. The crags and hollows in the left foreground represent limestone exposed by an earlier glaciation and so subjected to a much longer period of weathering and karstification. The remaining shale cap of Slieve Elva forms the gentle slope on the right.

C12. Ballyelly (M 150056)

Looking back southwards from a few hundred metres north of the fork affords a fine view of the sedgey shale slopes and the abrupt change from the level platform at its foot to the more dissected landscape further out. The track continues north-eastwards across an extensive, rather featureless area of limestone pavement. Passing the crest of the hill the limestone surface becomes more dissected, with small shallow closed depressions. As the track begins to descend more steeply it affords fine views across the Caher Valley to the extensive pavements and terraces of Gleninagh Mountain and the surrounding hills, while to the south can be seen the conifer covered shale cap of Poulacapple in the distance and the limestone terraces below extending northwards.

C13. Caher Valley (M 173068)

Descending to the valley floor the track joins a minor road which crosses over the Caher River, the largest perennial stream to flow across the limestone of the Burren. The water stays on the surface largely because much of the river bed is sealed with boulder clay, but also because of its steep descent against the southward dip of the limestone, giving the water less opportunity to percolate away along fractures. The water is saturated with calcium carbonate which is reprecipitated as a white crust on many stones on the river bed. Larger boulders are covered with the greenish-black moss *Cinclidotus fontinaloides* which thrives in limestone habitats which are intermittently flooded **(see back cover)**.

Nearby is the Caher Valley Nature Reserve **(Stop 13a)** (Grid ref. M 172064), where areas of limestone pavement and riverbank are interspersed with areas of typical Burren vegetation.

P - there is ample parking for visitors to the Nature Reserve. Further details about the Reserve, and of tours around it, can be obtained from the information centre at the Admiral's Rest, on the coast road at Craggagh (M 126057), about 3.5 km south of Fanore Bridge.

C14. Gleninagh - Poulacapple ridge (M 183071)

The Burren Way passes through a col on the long ridge, extending south from Gleninagh Mountain to Poulacapple, which separates the Caher Valley to the west from the valley of the Rathborney River to the east. The crest of this col is of bare or grassy limestone pavement studded with 'mini dolmens' built by passing walkers. The walls on either side of the track here are constructed of angular slabs of limestone. In contrast the lower slopes, both on the east and west flanks, are draped with grass-covered boulder clay deposited by the retreating ice sheets. The dry stone walls on these lower slopes are very different here from those on top, being constructed of rounded boulders, mostly of limestone but sometimes of granite, taken from the boulder clay itself.

C15. Rathborney River

This is one of very few surface rivers on the limestone outcrop of the Burren, although it is a misfit stream quite out of proportion to the deep valley it now occupies between Gleninagh Mountain to the west and Cappanawalla to the east. Over much of its length the river flows over thick deposits of boulder clay which fill most of the valley to a depth of at least 30 metres. At the southern end of the valley, where the road swings around to the east, these boulder clay deposits end abruptly at a steep grassy slope, with the almost sheer crag just to the east of this slope indicating the true depth of the valley. The river usually sinks in a muddy hollow a few hundred metres east of the Lisdoonvarna Road and about 3 km south of Ballyvaghan. In wet weather this is unable to take all of the flow, sometimes causing extensive flooding in the Ballyvaghan valley.

C16. Newtown Castle (M 217065)

There are few karst features of note to be seen from the Burren Way over the last few kilometres into Ballyvaghan. In wet weather small turloughs can be seen to the east of the track just north of Newtown Castle, but little can be seen of them in summer. However, the 1.3 km long Newtown Trail presents an opportunity to explore the lower slopes of Cappanawalla, immediately west of this section of the Burren Way. Leaflets giving further details can be obtained from Newtown Castle.

P - there is ample parking for visitors to Newtown Castle, but parking space is otherwise very restricted on the narrow lanes in this area.

C17. Ballyvaghan Harbour (M 231083)

A low cliff of boulder clay lies on the east side of the harbour, below the road leading to the quay. It is typical of the material left behind by the last glacial advance, with abundant fragments of limestone, and occasionally granite, 'floating' in a greyish-brown clay. Boulders of granite a metre or more across litter the shore below the cliff and other large granite boulders have been built into dry stone walls around the village. They are relatively common here at the foot of the northern scarp of the Burren but are much more scarce further to the south.

P - there is plenty of parking in the village.

Figure 22. Looking into the open pothole of Poulnagollum (Stop D8), on the eastern flank of Slieve Elva. This ancient stream sink now lies about 100 metres out from the shale edge which has been eroded back since the sink first formed. Passages leading off from the foot of this pothole provide access to more than 14 km of cave passages, the longest cave system in Ireland.

Excursion D. The Slieve Elva Circuit

The shale-capped hills of Slieve Elva and Knockauns Mountain are ringed by a series of minor roads and rough tracks which are ideal for exploring the limestone landscapes on foot or by bicycle (**Excursion Map 3**). The western side of this circuit follows the Burren Way for several kilometres and hence details of several sites are covered in that excursion (**Excursion C, stops C7-C11**). The starting point for the Slieve Elva Circuit itself is Lisdoonvarna. There is only very limited parking for cars at a few points elsewhere along the route.

D1. Coolagh River sink and dry valley (M 126014)

The Coolagh River flows south-west from the shale slopes on the western flank of Slieve Elva and sinks at the bottom of a deep depression where it has cut through to the limestone below, just north of a minor road. Although this appears to mark the end of the river valley (such entrenched sinks are often called '**blind valleys**'), a shallow valley can be traced across the minor road and onwards to the south-west. This valley deepens into the gorge which passes to the south of Ballynalackan Castle (**Stop A2**) and represents the former course of the Coolagh River before it was captured underground. In extreme floods the cave passages beneath the valley are unable to carry the full flow and the sink fills up before overflowing to pour down this ancient river course once again.

D2-D6. (= C7-C11). Knockauns Mountain and western Slieve Elva

Turn right on joining the Burren Way and head north-east. The next five stops are described in **Excursion C, stops C7 to C11**.

D7. South-east from Tobar an Athar Calbach holy well (M 151053)

From the holy well follow the track eastwards, skirting around the shale edge past many small sedgey hollows, before the track swings south-east along the eastern flank of Slieve Elva. There are numerous small sinks, and a few larger ones, at intervals along the shale margin on the north-eastern side of Slieve Elva; often the only evidence of these is the sound of falling water among the bushes. All drain into the vast Poulnagollum-Poulelva cave system (>14 km long) extending south along the east flank of Slieve Elva.

D8. Poulnagollum (M 161037)

Where the rough track meets the minor road heading south, turn sharply north for a short distance. Just beyond a triangular roadside parking space a rusty metal post marks a stile over the wall. Crossing the small field brings you to the lip of Poulnagollum pothole (**see Figure 22**), from which project the branches of a large Ash tree growing on the floor of the pothole some 10 metres below. On the far side a waterfall cascades into a hole in the floor, while nearby cave passages lead further into this complex cave system. Poulnagollum is an ancient stream sink which now lies some distance from the shale margin as a result of erosion of the shale. **Poulnagollum pothole and the passages leading from it should not be entered except by experienced cavers.**
P - there is limited parking near Pollnagollum pothole.

D9. Killeany Rising and Owentoberlea Sink (M 164007)

This is the main rising for virtually all of the water sinking along the eastern side of Slieve Elva into the Poulnagollum cave system, and most of that sinking on the western side of Poulacapple into the Cullaun caves. In dry weather all of the water sinks again just north of the bridge but in extreme flood a surface river may flow from here all the way to St. Brendan's Well and into the Gowlaun River.

D10. Upper St. Brendan's Rising (R 153987)

This is a flood rising for the water sinking on eastern Slieve Elva and western Poulacapple. There is little to see here except after heavy and prolonged rain, when a surface river may flow all the way down to St. Brendan's Well.

D11. St. Brendan's Well and the Gowlaun River (R 145985)

In dry weather this is the lowest rising for the water from Poulnagollum, which sinks in the Owentoberlea River, and that from the caves on the south-west side of Poulacapple. The water finally emerges at the lowest point where the limestone dips beneath the overlying shale. The rising itself cannot be seen from the road but a large stream flows under the bridge even when the river bed visible further upstream is quite dry. After prolonged or heavy rain a torrent may flow along this normally dry bed.

Figure 23. The Gowlaun River in flood. St Brendan's Well lies beneath the trees in the extreme lower right of the picture. The slopes are of Clare Shale but the river has cut down to flow on the top of the limestone beneath. In normal weather the river bed is dry upstream of St. Brendan's Well.

Excursion E. Aillwee and Poulnabrone

This excursion (**Excursion Map 1**) makes an interesting alternative to **stops A10-A12 of Excursion A**. About 1.5 km south-west of Ballyvaghan the road for Kilfenora and Aillwee Cave bears off to the left. Other than the minor road which leads up to Aillwee cave itself, the same road is followed all the way to Leamaneh Castle, then west to Kilfenora and, from there, north-west to Lisdoonvarna. From Leamaneh Castle to Kilfenora the route is the same as the first three stops of **Excursion F**, in reverse.

E1. Aillwee Cave (M 233048)

This is the only cave in the Burren readily accessible to the general public but it is well worth a visit and remains one of the most enigmatic karst features of the region. Perhaps the most striking feature throughout much of the cave is the superb phreatic half-tube in the roof. This lies at about the level of the clay band forming the lowest of the nine terraces in the Burren and cave formation probably was influenced by its impermeable nature. The passage shape shows that the cave formed originally beneath the local water table yet it now lies at an altitude of more than 90 metres above the floor of the Ballyvaghan valley below, suggesting that it formed at a time when the landscape was very different from that of today.

The half-tube increases in diameter as various tributary passages join it, from less than a metre near the entrance to more than 2 metres in the furthest part of the show cave. At several places the bedding plane immediately below the half-tube shows a network of much smaller intertwining half-tubes, known as **anastomoses**. The main tube probably developed through preferential enlargement of one of these 'proto caves'. Scallops in the half-tube are very indistinct but show that water was flowing into the hill. However, the active stream beyond the show cave now flows *outwards*. Dye tests have failed to reveal where this water comes from or where it goes.

When originally discovered the entrance passage was almost full to the roof with sediment; the level of this is clearly visible as a distinct line along the walls at about head-height. At several points further into the cave percolating water has washed away much of this sediment fill to reveal a deep canyon passage. Since this canyon lies below the bedding plane on which the half-tube, and small 'proto-caves', initially formed, it must have been produced by a stream which cut down into the floor once the local water table had fallen below the level of the half-tube, and so is clearly a vadose canyon (**see figures 13 and 14**). Stalactites and stalagmites have formed in places where water has percolated down fractures from the limestone surface above; dating of these shows that the vadose canyon below the half-tube was already well developed more than 350,000 years ago. In the final section of the show cave water cascades down into the passage from a hole in the roof; this is a vadose shaft that also has formed since the half-tube was drained by the fall in the water table.

The exit tunnel, although artificial, intercepted several sections of natural cave passage during its construction and these can still be seen.

P - there is ample parking at this major visitor attraction.

49

E2. Gragan East (M 223036)

Rejoining the main route the road south ascends, from the rich pasture on the boulder clay covering the floor and lower slopes of the Ballyvaghan Valley, onto an extensive area of gently sloping limestone pavement overlooking the head of the valley.
P - there is rough parking by the roadside here.

E3. Glensleade (M 230012)

The road passes southwards onto a much more deeply dissected area of limestone, contrasting with the smoother surface to the north. West of the road lies an enormous irregular closed depression, or uvala, up to 30 metres deep and covering more than 1.5 km². To the east of the road south from here are many small closed depressions and, visible in the crags a little further east, are several small gorges extending to the north-east. All of these point to a long history of karstification in this part of the Burren.

E4. Poulnabrone Dolmen (M 236004)

Although one of the most heavily visited sites on the Burren, the fine karst features visible around, and even on, this archaeological monument are overlooked by most visitors. Immediately east of the road is a large, sub circular, rock-walled doline about 10 metres deep **(see Figure 8)**, with other, shallower, grass-floored, dolines on either side of the road nearby. The immediate area of the dolmen is of typical limestone pavement with very prominent north-south jointing. Some of the major joints now form grass-floored avenues

Figure 24. Kamenitzas (solution pans) on the capstone of Poulnabrone Dolmen (Stop E4). Although the capstone is tilted, the kamenitza floors are horizontal, showing that they have formed since the dolmen was built.

between areas of pavement while a rather larger and deeper gully to the east of the dolmen can be followed north to where it divides into two still larger gullies extending to the north and north-east. The sill-stone at the entrance to the dolmen chamber was placed in an east-west grike and hence the dolmen itself is orientated roughly parallel with the main joint set. The dolmen's capstone has a noticeable slope to the south yet the small solution pans, or kamenitzas, on top have horizontal floors showing that they have formed since the dolmen was constructed about 5,800 years ago **(see Figure 24)**.
P - it is usually safe to park by the roadside here.

E5. Carran Church (R 240974)

This 15th Century church and small graveyard overlook the vast elongate closed depression which extends some 2 km north-east to Meggagh **(see Stop F7)** and is up to 70 metres deep. Its rocky slopes and cliffs are, in places, buried beneath grassy slopes developed on boulder clay, demonstrating that the depression is older than the last glacial.
P - park close to the side of the road.

South from Carran Church the road intercepts the route of **Excursion F** at Sheshymore (between **Stops F3 and F4**).

Figure 25. Looking north across the uvala at Kilcorney (Stop F8). The sinuous drainage channel ends just short of the entrance to the Cave of the Wild Horses, which lies at the foot of the cliffs in the right foreground.

51

Excursion F. Kilfenora-Carran Circuit

This circuit (**Excursion Map 1**) passes through some of the large scale karst landforms which are characteristic of the south-eastern portion of the Burren. The most conspicuous of these are the large closed depressions, lacking any surface inlet or outlet, which represent the diagnostic features of karst landscapes. These enormous irregular dolines, sometimes also known as uvalas, may originally have developed as what are called '**karst windows**', where holes eroded through a former shale cover concentrated drainage onto the underlying limestone. Some of the best examples in the Burren are visited on this excursion. The route is best followed by bike or small car, since part of it follows fairly narrow roads and there is very limited parking at most places.

F1. East of Kilfenora

The road for 4 to 5 km east of Kilfenora mostly lies on the top of the limestone and just north of the shale edge. Classic 'basket-of-eggs' drumlin topography is a very obvious feature of the land to the south of the road. These drumlins were formed by glacial moulding of the boulder clay towards the end of the last glaciation.

F2. Ballyclancahill sink (R 218933)

An artificially straightened stream has incised deeply into the eastern end of a long flat field, crossed by wooden pylons, to sink just south of the road. Conspicuous collapse hollows in the soil nearby act as flood overflow sinks but in winter a temporary lake may form, with centuries of accumulated lake sediment forming the flat floor of the field.

F3. Leamaneh Castle sink (R 235934)

A minor stream sinks on the south side of the road opposite Leamaneh Castle, though there is little to see in dry weather.

F4. Lough Aleenaun (R 249954)

Near the south-western end of the minor road to Carran there are fine views southwards to the closed depression which (sometimes) contains Lough Aleenaun. A low drumlin on the south side of the depression has impounded the lake, which is fed by springs emerging from a low crag on its north side and drains via several sinks at the lake margins. In wet weather it can fill to a depth of 3-4 metres in only a few hours, but it may drain completely after little more than a week of dry weather.

F5. large doline (R 253963)

A kilometre east of the road junction a large doline, or closed depression (**see Figure 8**), lies to the north of the road. Dolines like this are perhaps the most typical feature of karst landscapes. This one has cliffed walls up to 10 metres high and an undulating grassy floor, perhaps underlain by boulder clay left by the last glaciation. It might seem odd that glaciation did not destroy dolines like this or fill them completely with boulder clay. Probably they were occupied by stagnant ice over which the main ice sheets moved, thereby minimising any erosion or infilling.

F6. Carran Depression (R 285985)

As the road descends northwards it affords magnificent views across the Carran Depression. With an area of more than 7 km^2 this is the largest closed depression on the Burren. The Croide na boirne pub and restaurant (Grid ref. R 278987) is also an excellent spot to view this area. The floor of much of the depression is strikingly flat with a sluggish stream, the Castletown River, flowing across it. Layers of chert in the limestone beneath, and several metre thick deposits of boulder clay and lake sediments, keep the stream on the surface despite its altitude of more than 110 metres above sea level. It finally sinks at the southern end of the depression, to reappear from springs on the Fergus River more than 6 km to the south. In wet weather the sinks are unable to take all of the flow and the floor of the depression floods, often for several months. In effect it is a turlough and is the highest in Ireland. The sides of the depression rise steeply to altitudes of more than 200 metres, in places draped with grass-covered patches of boulder clay.
P - there is ample parking around the village.

F7. Meggagh (R 255987)

The road opposite the Croide na boirne pub climbs steeply to a gently undulating plateau of grassy limestone pavement but after less than 2 km it plunges spectacularly some 70 metres into the Meggagh depression. This is a classic closed depression, the diagnostic landform of karst landscapes. In wet weather a temporary lake forms in the lowest part, fed by numerous springs and draining via sinks to Lough Aleenaun to the south (**Stop F4**). The southern end of this depression can be viewed from Carran Church (**Stop E5**).

F8. Kilcorney (R 225995)

This has a much more irregular shape than either of the preceding depressions and steeper sides which form cliffs in many places. It is also unusual in being associated with a large cave system, the Cave of the Wild Horses, with more than 800 metres of explored passages descending to 58 metres below the floor of the depression. The entrance lies at the foot of the cliff south of the ruined church and there are other fragments of large passage higher in the cliffs nearby. **Only experienced cavers should attempt to explore the main cave.** The grassy floor of the main depression is fairly flat but a sinuous channel meanders across it from a boulder-filled hollow near the middle to end in a boulder-filled depression at the foot of the cliff just north of the cave entrance (**see Figure 26**). After prolonged wet weather the Kilcorney depression and the Cave of the Wild Horses may fill rapidly from below. Noises associated with this flooding may perhaps have given rise to the name of the cave. The water subsequently drains back into the cave via the sinuous channel.
P - there is parking space for only one or two cars near the ruined church here.

F9. South to Kilfenora

The final part of the route follows the limestone-shale boundary for some distance, with rush-covered shale slopes to the west and grassy limestone pavement to the east. The shale margin swings away south-west at one point but rejoins the road further south.

53

Excursion G: The Gort Lowlands

At first sight the Gort lowlands appear as a monotonous expanse of low ground, dotted with lakes in its southern part and sandwiched between the Burren uplands and Galway Bay to the west, and the Slieve Aughty Mountains to the east. But another glance at the map reveals a remarkable lack of surface drainage. Only a few disjointed fragments of surface river are evident around Gort (much of the Dunkellin River, near Craughwell, is artificial) and most of the lakes have no surface inlet or outlet. In fact a huge, complex karst drainage system lies beneath the area and goes largely unnoticed except when prolonged heavy rain overwhelms the subterranean passages to cause extensive flooding.

The Old Red Sandstone uplands of the Slieve Aughty Mountains form a major catchment from which three principal rivers drain onto the limestone. To the north the Owenshree River flows along the foot of the scarp for several kilometres before sinking just north of Peterswell. A little further south the Boleyneendorish River meanders westwards for a short distance across the limestone before bifurcating to enter the aptly named 'Hammerhead Sinks' south-west of Peterswell. To the south the Owendalulleegh River flows through Lough Cutra, changing its name to the Gort River before sinking at the Punch Bowl. The river is seen again at the surface at various points between here and Coole Lough but, other than in exceptional floods, water does not flow on the surface any further west.

The various sites covered by this excursion **(Excursion Map 4)** are scattered across quite a large area; hence it is necessary to cycle or drive if all of them are to be visited in the same day. Anyone visiting this area would be well advised to see the natural history audio-visual display at the Coole Visitor Centre at Coole Park (Grid ref. M 439049; Stop G7). This gives an excellent account of the workings of the turloughs and underground drainage system, and its importance for wildlife.

G1. Cappacasheen (M 3804)

The vast expanse of low-lying, seemingly featureless, limestone pavement on either side of the road here contrasts strikingly with the eastern scarp of the Burren rising steeply just a short distance to the west. As such it is a fine example of a corrosion plain, formed by several million years of dissolutional lowering of the exposed limestone.

G2. Lough Bunny (M 380968)

Lough Bunny is a permanent lake but has no surface inlets or outlets. It is fed by numerous small springs, which in wet weather can be seen emerging from fissures along the east shore, and drains via sinks at its northern end en route towards Coole Lough. Much of the eastern shore of the lough is formed on limestone bedding planes which dip gently to the west **(see Figure 26)**. The lake water is permanently saturated with calcium carbonate and so the lower parts of the lake shore are relatively smooth, without any of the typical limestone pavement features seen away from the lake, and are coated with a soft crust of chalky 'marl'.

P - there is a small car park on the landward side of the road towards the eastern end of the lough.

Figure 26. Gently dipping limestone on the east shore of Lough Bunny (Stop G2). Small solution pits cover the upper shore, which is exposed all year, but when the lower shore is exposed in summer it is protected from weathering by a chalky 'marl' crust. The lake water itself is too saturated with carbonate to dissolve the lower shore directly, which remains smooth. The eastern scarp of the Burren is visible in the distance, rising abruptly from the Gort lowlands.

G3. The Punch Bowl (M 455002)

The Gort River flows west to a major sink, the Punch Bowl, through a steep-sided gorge cut into a thick cover of boulder clay; it is a classic example of a blind valley. A little west of the main sink is a large and deep depression formed by collapse into the passage beneath. Continued solution of the limestone and washing away of slumped material by the underground river will eventually create an open shaft down to the river itself, such as has happened at The Churn some 600 metres further west.

The water from the Punch Bowl flows underground only a short distance before reappearing at the head of another deep gorge, or **steephead**, incised into the boulder clay south of the lane. It sinks again at Blackweir, by the junction of the lane with the main Ennis Road (N18). A few hundred metres west of the Ennis Road lie the Churn and the Ladle, two collapse shafts more than ten metres deep dropping straight into the underground river. Cave divers have discovered that the river passage lies 34 metres beneath the water surface in the Churn and have followed it for about 140 metres downstream towards Cannahowna Cave **(Stop G4)** still further to the west.

P - there is a small car park in the lane near the Punch Bowl, with further parking in the lay-by adjacent to the Blackweir sink.

G4. Cannahowna Cave [Pollduagh] (M 457003)

Cannahowna Cave, also known as Pollduagh, lies on the north side of the small lane which heads west from the Ennis Road (N18) opposite the lane to the Punch Bowl. A wide path descends a short distance to the river and to a small jetty projecting across the cave entrance. The river last seen on the east side of the Ennis Road, and intercepted by the Churn, reappears here from an imposing cave passage more than 10 metres wide and 3 metres high **(Figure 27)**. The roof of the main cave descends gradually upstream, dipping below the water some 50 metres in from the entrance. Cave divers have followed the river upstream for a further 250 metres, to a depth of 30 metres. In flood the river extends the full width of this entrance, but in low water conditions the river can be crossed to reach a smaller passage which carries the main flow at such times; its tubular shape is clear evidence that it formed under phreatic conditions, below the local water table. **This smaller cave is an important bat roost and should not be entered**.

The course of the Gort River westwards from the limestone margin represents an ancient karst drainage route which in places looped to a considerable depth below the surface. Shallower parts of the system have been destroyed by erosion and surface rivers now connect the remaining fragments. The deeper loops, such as that immediately upstream of Cannahowna Cave, have survived as fragmented remnants of a once much more extensive cave system. However, they too are being slowly destroyed as is shown by the collapse feature associated with the Punch Bowl and the open shafts of the Churn and Ladle.

P - very limited parking at the roadside, so tuck in close to the hedge.

Figure 27. The imposing entrance of Cannahowna Cave, or Pollduagh (Stop G4), an underground loop of the Gort River.

G5. Blackrock Turlough (M 500080)

The Owenshree River flows south-west along the foot of the Slieve Aughty Mountains to sink in a deep closed depression at Blackrock. In summer it is a grassy hollow dotted with boulders covered with the characteristic Black Turlough Moss, *Cinclidotus fontinaloides* (see back cover), from which the townland probably derives its name. Following winter rains the sinks are rapidly overwhelmed to form a vast lake. In the severe floods of 1995 this reached a maximum depth of almost 14 metres at one stage, flooding the road just to the south.

G6. Kiltartan Rising (M 450055)

The Gort River reappears at a major rising below a low bluff in the field immediately south of Kiltartan Church. It meanders northwestwards for several hundred metres, en route passing underground again for a few metres before entering another major sink at the foot of a drumlin (a low rounded hill of boulder clay). It reappears less than 300 metres to the west and flows southwestwards into Coole Lough.
P - there is a large car park opposite the church.

G7. Coole Lough (M 430040)

At first sight Coole Lough appears little different from many other lakes in Ireland but this belies its significance as the 'hub' of a vast and complex underground drainage system. The drainage from the three main rivers flowing off the Slieve Aughty Mountains to the east, and from several of the lakes to the south, ultimately converges on Coole Lough. The lake has no surface outlet; instead the water passes underground on the west side of the lake in a large, boulder-choked sink. In summer this sink can easily cope with the volume of water flowing into the lake and the water level may fall until only a shallow channel meanders slowly from the main perennial lake to the sink. Only the abundance of the Black Turlough Moss, *Cinclidotus fontinaloides*, covering the boulders and trunks of trees along the woodland edge overlooking the lough (see back cover) hint at the seasonal changes in water level. In winter, when the ground is saturated and rainfall is high, the sink is overwhelmed and the lake fills rapidly, often rising 5 metres or more. Under such conditions water flows into adjacent basins, such as Newtown Turlough to the south (Stop G8), via passages only a few metres below the surface. In the greatest floods, such as that of early 1995, surface rivers may even form between adjacent turloughs. The Coole Lough basin and surrounding turloughs act as a vast reservoir for excess flood water and only when the rate of inflow has fallen below the capacity of the outlet passage do water levels begin to fall again.
P - there is ample car parking adjacent to the Visitor Centre.

G8. Newtown Turlough (M 427022)

An impressive artificial causeway, built during the Famine, rises more than 5 metres above an area of low ground to the west of Gort and overlooks Newtown Turlough to the north. In dry summers it is a vast area of green pasture bounded by areas of slightly higher ground scattered with hawthorn bushes and patches of rough limestone pavement

Figure 28. Newtown Turlough (Stop G8) during dry weather in Summer.

(Figure 28). A small stream trickles sluggishly beneath the causeway and is joined by another small stream emanating from an enigmatic circular pool. After heavy rainfall the view is strikingly different **(Figure 29)**. Large volumes of water pour forth from the 'enigmatic pool' and are supplemented by the greatly increased volume of the stream, fed by springs to the south, and by several other major springs on the north side of the turlough which act as overflows from Coole Lough. Eventually the whole area may become a single vast lake **(Figure 30)** and in 1995 the causeway itself was submerged beneath more than 2 metres of floodwater!
P - there is very limited parking here - tuck in close to the wall.

G9. Hawkhill Turlough (M 411023)
This small turlough displays some of their classic features; the dry stone walls disappearing beneath the water surface in winter and the Black Turlough Moss which can be seen to cover them when water levels are low in summer. Strangely, during a cold spell in January 1997 Hawkhill Turlough remained completely ice-free while the adjacent Newtown Turlough was covered by several centimetres of ice.

G10. Garryland Nature Reserve (M 413036)
Various trails through Garryland Wood pass close to several turloughs within the Coole-Garryland turlough complex. In summer these appear as grassy glades or pastures within the woods, littered with the characteristic moss-blackened boulders, but in winter the

Figure 29. Newtown Turlough filling in late Autumn, after heavy rain.

Figure 30. Newtown Turlough in Winter. In extreme floods the photographer here would be under more than 2 metres of water!

geography of the area is completely changed as the depressions fill rapidly with water. Some of the risings can be an awesome sight in full flow following heavy rain.

P - there is limited parking at the nature reserve entrance on the western edge of Garryland Wood.

G11. Caherglassaun Lough (M 415063)

Caherglassaun Lough is a permanent lake with no surface inlet or outlet but shows the same seasonal fluctuations as the turloughs. The main inlet rising forms a conspicuous small embayment on the south shore, opposite the castle (which can be reached via a very rough track to the north of the lough), while the main sinks are at the northern end of the lough. Various collapse features are present around the lough, the largest lying immediately north of the castle. These collapses are associated with an enormous phreatic cave passage beneath. However, the most remarkable feature of this lough is that during dry spells water levels respond to the tides, even though the risings on the coast lie some 5 km away.

G12. Kinvarra Risings (M 380105)

At the southeastern end of the long inlet of Kinvarra Bay are a series of impressive intertidal risings, the largest of which lie between Dunguaire Castle and the small island

Figure 31. Intertidal rising near Dunguaire Castle, Kinvarra. This, and other springs on this stretch of coast, is the final destination of most of the water draining from the Gort area.

about 200 metres to the southwest (see **Figure 31**), with other springs at various points all along the coast to Kinvarra itself. The water appearing here has travelled underground from the Gort turlough complex via Coole Lough, though some is believed to drain from the eastern flanks of the Burren. The outflow is difficult to measure but is many hundreds, if not thousands, of litres per second even at low flow. In times of flood an obvious stream of freshwater can be seen flowing out into the bay, floating on the denser seawater. At low tide it is possible to cross to the small island, where remnants of a large, partly collapsed, cave passage can be seen crossing its southern end.

P - there is parking in the village and near Dunguaire Castle.

Other areas

The seven excursions described here are merely a selection chosen to encompass most of the common karst features of the Burren and the Gort lowlands, particularly along some of the more popular tourist routes. However, many of the karst features described in this book are found widely across the area and there are endless possibilities for further walks. For those wishing to follow their own routes, the introductory sections of this book can be used to interpret karst features you discover for yourself. Happy wandering!

Useful Addresses

For anyone with a deeper interest in the landscape of this area or who would like to explore some of the 'wild' caves of the Burren, three organisations have had a long association with the Burren and/or caving and are worth contacting.

British Cave Research Association

The Old Methodist Chapel, Great Hucklow, Buxton, Derbyshire SK17 8RG.
www.bcra.org.uk

The main cave and karst organisation in Britain, with a membership including many cavers as well as amateur and professional karst geomorphologists.

Speleological Union of Ireland

c/o Association for Adventure Sports (AFAS), House of Sport, Longmile Road, Walkinstown, Dublin 12.
www.cavingireland.org

The umbrella organisation for cavers in Ireland.

University of Bristol Spelaeological Society

Hon. Secretary, The Spelaeological Society, c/o Student Union, Queen's Road, Clifton, Bristol BS8 1LN.

Past and present members of UBSS have been active in the Burren and Gort area, both above and below ground, for more than 50 years. They have discovered many of the cave systems there and have produced much of the material published on the karst of this region.

Further reading

There are many weighty tomes on karst geomorphology but most are for the specialist. For those wishing to know more about this fascinating subject, the following offer a relatively inexpensive starting point.

Karst Geomorphology. *J.N.Jennings 1985.*
Blackwell, 283 pp. An excellent introduction to many aspects of the subject.

Karst Geomorphology and Hydrology. *Derek Ford and Paul Williams 1989.*
Unwin Hyman, 601 pp. One of the most comprehensive books available on the subject, though rather more for the specialist.

A Dictionary of Karst and Caves. *David Lowe and Tony Waltham 1995.*
British Cave Research Association Cave Studies Series no. 6, 40 pp. A useful guide to many technical terms.

Caves and Cave Life. *Philip Chapman 1993.*
New Naturalist Series, Harper Collins, 219 pp. A very readable account of caves and the animals and plants they sometimes contain.

Classic Landforms of the Burren. *David Drew 2001.*
The Geographical Association, 56 pp. A very useful general guide to some of the karst features of this region.

Aillwee Cave and the Caves of the Burren. *David Drew 1984*
Irish Heritage Series: 43. A simple attractive guide to this and other caves.

The Caves of Ireland. *J.C.Coleman 1965*
Anvil Books, Tralee, 88 pp. The only compilation of all Irish caves known at the time. Sadly now out of print.

Caves of County Clare. *C.A.Self (ed.) 1981.*
University of Bristol Spelaeological Society (UBSS), 225 pp. More a specialist guide book for cavers.

The Caves of North-West Clare, Ireland. *E.K.Tratman (ed.) 1969.*
University of Bristol Spelaeological Society, David & Charles, 256 pp. The most detailed published account of the Burren karst and caves. It is long out of print, but a new edition is being prepared by members of UBSS.

Index of Technical Terms

Only the principal page numbers where these terms are explained or referred to are given here.

anastomoses - an intertwining network of small phreatic tubes, or 'proto caves' *(p 49)*

bedding plane - a nearly horizontal (at least in the Burren) break in a rock sequence formed by original variations in depositional conditions. *(p 11 & fig 4)*

biokarst - a general term for various pinnacles and pits formed on limestone by biological processes (bioerosion). Often well-developed in the intertidal zone. *(p 16-17 & fig 9)*

blind valley - a stream valley which has a blind ending, rather like a cul de sac, where the stream sinks underground. *(p 47)*

boulder clay - jumbled debris of clay and rock left behind by glaciers. *(p 6 & fig 5)*

Carboniferous - a period of geological time during which the rocks of the Burren were deposited; from about 360-290 million years ago.

chert - an impure type of flint, an amorphous form of the mineral silica. *(p 9)*

clint - limestone block surrounded by solutional fissures (grikes) on limestone pavement. *(p 14 & fig 6)*

Devonian - a period of geological time during which the rocks forming much of the Slieve Aughty Mountains were deposited; about 410-360 million years ago.

doline - a surface depression entirely enclosed by higher ground; the characteristic landform of karst. On rocks other than limestone such depressions would form lakes. *(p 14 & fig 8)*

dolomite - a rock type formed of calcium and magnesium carbonates. *(p 7)*

drumlin - a rounded hill of boulder clay moulded by the movement of ice over it. *(pp 48-49)*

erratic - a boulder or smaller piece of rock transported from its original location by ice movement. *(pp 10 & 14 & fig 7)*

fault - a fracture on which movement of the rocks either side has occurred. *(p 10)*

flowstone - calcium carbonate redeposited on walls or floor by percolating water. *(p 22 & fig 16)*

glacial striae -scratches formed by the passage of ice across bare rock. *(p 12 & fig 5)*

glaciokarst - a karst landscape strongly influenced by the effects of previous glaciation. *(pp 6 & 13)*

grike - a solutionally widened vertical fracture separating clints on a limestone pavement. *(p 14, fig 6 & Inside Back Cover)*

joint - a vertical fracture in the rocks caused by earth movements, but along which there has been no movement of the rocks on either side. *(p 11 & fig 4)*

kamenitza - a solution pan or shallow pool on limestone. *(p 14, figs 6 & 24)*

karst - the general term for landscapes formed by weathering of soluble rocks; named after a region of Slovenia. *(p 5)*

karst window - a hole eroded through an impermeable cover rock, such as shale, to expose a patch of limestone beneath; effectively a window onto the underlying rock. *(p 52)*

limestone - a rock type made largely of calcium carbonate. Unlike most rocks, it is weakly soluble in water. *(p 8)*

palaeokarst - literally 'ancient karst'; karst that formed many millions of years ago and was buried by later deposition of rock. *(p 11 & fig 20)*

paragenesis - a process of cave formation in which passages below the water table enlarge upwards by solution because their floors are protected by sediment deposits. *(p 19, figs 11, 14, 17 & 19)*

photokarren (photokarst) - light-orientated karst features formed by the interaction of endolithic algae (living within the surface layer of the rock) with limestone. *(pp 15 & 35)*

phreatic - below the water table. *(p 19 & fig 11)*

phreatic tube - tube-like cave passage formed below the water table by equal dissolution of roof, walls and floor. *(p 19, figs 11, 15 & 20)*

rillenkarren - narrow, sharp-edged solution grooves which form on steep limestone faces. *(p 14 & fig 6)*

rinnenkarren - rather broad, rounded-edged solution runnels which form on more gently sloping limestone. *(p 14 & Front Cover)*

rising (resurgence or spring) - the point where an underground stream emerges at the surface again. *(p 19, figs 11 & 31)*

scallops - asymmetric, scoop-shaped hollows formed by water flowing over a soluble rock. *(p 21 & fig 12)*

schist - a foliated or flakey type of metamorphic rock common in Connemara.

shale - mudstone which has been compressed to form a thinly layered, or laminated, rock. Shale is impervious to water, which instead flows on the surface. *(p 7)*

sink (swallow hole) - the point where a stream passes underground. *(p 18 & fig 11)*

slickenside - scratches formed by two rock masses moving past each other on a fault. *(pp 10-12 & 37)*

stalactites - straw-shaped or tapering masses of calcium carbonate deposited on a cave roof by percolating water. *(p 22 & fig 16)*

stalagmites - often rounded or conical masses of calcium carbonate deposited on a cave floor by dripping percolation water. *(p 22 & fig 16)*

steephead - the abrupt, and usually steep-walled, head of a valley which lies behind some risings or springs. *(p 55)*

tufa - a rather porous form of calcium carbonate often deposited by small springs in limestone regions.

turlough - literally 'dry lake'; a seasonal lake in which both inlet and outlet are underground. *(p 15, figs 28-30, & Back Cover)*

uvala - term used for large and complex dolines. *(p 15, 51 & fig 25)*

vadose - above the water table. *(p 19 & fig 11)*

vadose canyon/trench - a trench or canyon-like passage formed by a cave stream cutting down into a passage floor in the vadose zone. *(p 19, figs 11, 13 & 16)*

vadose shaft - a vertical cave passage formed by a cave stream falling down a fracture under gravity. *(p 19 & fig 11)*